Table of Contents

The Fairy Ring

You may have seen circles of mushrooms on your lawn after a rain. People in England call the circles "fairy rings," for they believe fairies dance inside them.

When the moon shines, the people say, fairies come out of the forest. They play music on flutes and bells and dance in the fairy rings all night long. If human people walk outside at night, they may hear the fairy music. It is so beautiful that they may follow the sound to the fairy ring. But if they step inside the ring, they must dance with the fairies. The dance only seems to last for a few minutes. But every minute people spend inside the ring makes them seven years older. When the fairies finally let the people go, they are old.

One story tells about what happened to a young man named Shon. One night Shon heard fairy music and stopped to listen. He stepped inside a fairy ring, and the fairies took him into their dance. He tried to get away, and after a little while he crawled to the edge of the ring. He managed to put his finger outside the ring. As soon as he did, the spell was broken. He ran home and knocked at the door for his wife to let him in. But instead an old man opened the door.

"Who are you?" asked the old man.

"My name is Shon. Where are my wife and my son?"

"Shon was my grandfather," the old man said. "I have heard he went away when he was young and never came back!"

Then Shon knew what had happened. He had spent many years dancing in the fairy ring, and now he was a very old man. He went into the woods and was never seen again.

Think About It
Would you step inside a fairy ring? Why or why not?

Name _____

The Fairy Ring

Main Idea

1. Choose another title for the story.

_____ A Magical Dance

_____ Shon Becomes a Grandfather

_____ A Circle of Mushrooms

Sequencing

2. Number the events below in the order that they happened.

_____ He stepped inside the fairy ring.

_____ Shon heard the fairy music.

_____ He ran back to his home and knocked on the door.

_____ He escaped from the fairy ring.

_____ Shon discovered he had become a very old man.

Reading for Details

3. Use the clues to answer the questions.

Who calls a circle of mushrooms a "fairy ring"? (paragraph 1) _____

When do the fairies come out of the forest? (paragraph 2) _____

_____

What do people follow to the fairy ring? (paragraph 2) _____

Where did Shon run as soon as he escaped from the fairy ring? (paragraph 3) _____

_____

Why was Shon a very old man at the end of the story? (paragraph 7) _____

_____

Reading for Understanding

4. Circle **yes** or **no**.

People say that I play music on whistles and drums.	Yes	No
People say that I dance all night long.	Yes	No
People say that one of my minutes is the same as seven of your years.	Yes	No

The Foolish Coyote

In the fall of the year the blackbirds always gathered on top of a mountain to sing and dance before they went south for the winter. One day a coyote was hunting on the mountain. He heard the blackbirds singing, and when he looked up he saw them flying in the air.

"How beautifully you fly and dance!" the coyote cried. "Can you teach me to do that? If I could fly, I could be the great king of the coyotes."

The blackbirds knew the coyote could never fly. But they thought they would have some fun. So they called back, "We can teach you to fly. Come to the top of the mountain and we will help you."

When the coyote got to the mountain top, the birds told him to sit down. Then each bird pulled a feather from its wing. "This will hurt," said the birds. "But this is the only way you will be able to fly."

They stuck the feathers into the coyote's legs and tail. The feathers pricked terribly, but the coyote said nothing. He sat very still until the birds had finished, all the while thinking of what a great king he would be.

When all the feathers were in place, the excited coyote ran to the edge of the mountain and jumped into the air. For a minute he seemed to be flying. He flapped his legs and looked at the ground far below.

"Look at me!" he shouted. "I'm king of the coyotes!"

But then he began to fall, and finally he landed with a crash on the ground. As he lay there sore and bruised, he realized that it is wisdom and courage, not the ability to fly, that makes a great king.

Name _____

The Foolish Coyote

Main Idea

1. What is the main idea of this story?

_____ The coyote wanted to be king.

_____ The coyote was a hunter.

_____ The blackbirds tricked the coyote.

Sequencing

2. Number the events below in the order that they happened.

_____ The blackbirds stuck feathers into the coyote.

_____ The coyote crashed to the ground.

_____ He asked the blackbirds to teach him how to fly.

_____ The coyote was hunting on the mountain.

_____ The coyote jumped off the mountain and seemed to fly.

Reading for Details

3. Use the clues to answer the questions.

When did the blackbirds gather on top of the mountain? (paragraph 1) _____

_____

Where did each blackbird pull a feather from? (paragraph 4)_____

_____

Why did the blackbirds say they would help the coyote? (paragraph 3)_____

_____

Reading for Understanding

4. Write the word or phrase that is used in the story.

How did the blackbirds fly and dance? _____

_____

How did the coyote feel when he ran to the edge of the mountain? _____

How did the coyote land on the ground? _____

_____

A Boy Named Maui

Once on an island there lived a little boy named Maui. Maui had four older brothers who were much bigger and stronger than he was. But the brothers were lazy. They made Maui and his mother do all the work while they laid around in the sun. Because he worked so hard, Maui's mother liked him best of all her children. So the brothers were jealous of Maui and wanted to shame him.

One night the brothers said, "Let's get up early tomorrow morning and go fishing. But we won't tell Maui. When we get back, we shall say that Maui was lazy and wouldn't come with us. Then Mother will not like him."

But the brothers didn't know that Maui had magic powers. He had heard their plans, so he made a magic fishhook from a piece of bone. Then he hid in the bottom of the fishing boat under some mats. The next morning, when the brothers paddled far out into the sea, they were surprised to see Maui come out from hiding.

"Now," said Maui, "let us fish." He threw his magic fishhook and his line into the water. Up from the sea came not a fish, but a huge island. The island was the home of the mighty sea god. When the four older brothers saw the beautiful island, each one wanted to be its king, and they started to fight. They fought so hard over who was to be king that the island broke in two, and all the lazy brothers were drowned!

Then the sea god came to Maui and said, "I give this island to you. Please be its king." But Maui didn't want to be king. So he gave the island to his people. Today, that island is called New Zealand, and Maui's people ruled the island for hundreds of years.

Think About It

Pretend that you have just received magical powers which only work if you use them in a friendly way. What will you do?

Maui is pronounced Mou'ē.

Name _____

A Boy Named Maui

Main Idea

1. Choose another title for this story.

_____ The Fight of the Five Brothers

_____ A Gift of an Island

_____ How New Zealand Was Made

Sequencing

2. Number the events below in the order that they happened.

_____ Maui caught an island with his magic hook.

_____ Maui's brothers made plans to shame him.

_____ Maui gave the island to his people.

_____ All the brothers went fishing.

Reading for Details

3. Use the clues to answer the questions.

Besides Maui, who did all the work? (paragraph 1)_____

What didn't Maui's brothers know about him? (paragraph 3)_____

_____

When did the brothers want to be king? (paragraph 4)_____

_____

Where did the sea god live? (paragraph 4)_____

Why did Maui give the island to his people? (paragraph 5)_____

_____

Reading for Understanding

4. List the word(s) that describe the character in the correct column.

	magical lazy		hard-working kind
	generous jealous		plays favorites smart
Maui	Brothers	Mother	Sea God
_____	_____	_____	_____
_____	_____	_____	_____
_____	_____	_____	_____
_____	_____	_____	_____

The Monkey and the Ogre

Once in India, there was a magic forest. In the middle of the lake in this forest lived a terrible ogre. Whenever any animal tried to drink from the lake, the ogre would jump out and gobble the animal up.

One day a band of monkeys came to the forest. Their leader was a wise old monkey who knew about the ogre. So he warned the others, "An ogre lives in the lake in this forest. If he catches you, he will eat you. Don't drink any water from the lake until I tell you it is safe."

The monkeys listened to their leader. They grew very thirsty, but they stood back from the lake. Then the wise old monkey went near the lake and waited to see if the ogre would appear.

When the ogre saw the old monkey, he stuck his head out of the water and said, "Come down to the water and drink."

"No," said the monkey. "If I come to the water, you will eat me."

"Yes," said the ogre. "But there is no other water in the forest. Soon you and your friends will have to come here to drink. Then I will eat you all."

The old monkey thought and thought. Then he saw some long hollow reeds growing near the lake. He picked the reeds and gave them to the other monkeys. Each monkey put one end of the reed in its mouth and the other end in the water. Then the monkeys sucked the water through the reeds. So they stayed away from the lake and still drank their fill. the ogre was so furious when he saw this, he disappeared into the lake with a roar! And none of the monkeys ever saw him again.

Think About It

Why do you think the wise old monkey was the leader of the other monkeys?

Name _____

The Monkey and the Ogre

Main Idea
1. Choose another title for this story.

_____ The Terrible Ogre

_____ How the Wise Monkey
Defeated The Ogre

_____ A Magic Forest

Sequencing
2. Number the events in the order that they happened.

_____ The wise monkey waited by the lake for the ogre.

_____ The ogre disappeared with a roar.

_____ The monkeys drank the water through hollow reeds.

_____ The ogre said he would eat all the monkeys.

Reading for Details
3. Use the clues to answer the questions.

Where was the magic forest? (paragraph 1) _____

What lived in the middle of the lake? (paragraph 1) _____

When did the ogre jump out of the lake? (paragraph 1) _____

_____

Who knew about the ogre? (paragraph 2) _____

Why did the monkeys use long, hollow reeds? (paragraph 7) _____

_____

Reading for Understanding
4. The monkey was able to outsmart the ogre because

_____ he thought before he acted.

_____ he was stronger than the ogre.

_____ the ogre wasn't watching.

When the Sun Went Away

In the old days, the people of Japan believed the sun goddess and the god of night were sister and brother. The sun goddess made the crops grow and the trees bloom, so the people loved her. But the god of night brought evil spirits to harm the land, and the people feared him.

Soon the god of night grew jealous of his sister. He wanted her to go away so he could keep the earth dark forever. So he thought of a plan. One day when the sun goddess was sitting in her temple, the god of night crept in with a big bag. When he opened the bag, a huge snake crawled out and coiled itself around the sun goddess' chair. She was so frightened that she ran into a cave and would not come out at all.

Now the earth was always dark. The god of night ruined the crops and frightened the people. Children were afraid to go out to play. So the people went to the cave to ask the sun goddess to come back to them.

"Please come out," they begged. "Your brother is destroying us." But still the sun goddess would not come out. So the people asked a wise man what to do.

"Make noise," he said. "Maybe she will be curious and come out to see what is happening."

So the people gathered at the cave. They beat drums, rang bells, and sang. The goddess heard the noise and became curious. Finally she crept to the mouth of the cave and peeked out. When the people saw her, they grabbed her hand and pulled her out. The earth became bright again, and the people danced for joy. When the god of night saw how happy the people were, he felt bad for having frightened his sister. And he promised never to do it again.

Think About It

Pretend that you are living long ago. Write a story to explain why there is thunder and lightning.

Name _____

When the Sun Went Away

Sequencing
1. Number the events below in the order that they happened.

_____ The god of night put a snake around his sister's chair.

_____ The sun goddess became curious and crept out of the cave.

_____ People gathered at the mouth of the cave and made noise.

_____ The sun goddess ran into the cave and would not come out.

Reading for Details
2. Use the clues to answer the questions.

Who gathered at the cave? (paragraph 6) _____

What did they do there? (paragraph 6) _____

When did they grab the goddess' hand? (paragraph 6) _____

Why did they dance for joy? (paragraph 6) _____

Main Idea
3. What is the main idea of the last paragraph of this story?

_____ The sun goddess came to the mouth of the cave.

_____ The sun god promised not to trick his sister again.

_____ The people were able to bring the sun goddess out of the cave.

Reading for Understanding
4. The people loved the sun goddess because _____

_____

_____

5. The people feared the god of night because _____

_____

_____

How People Were Made — A South American Legend

Long ago, the gods made the earth of rock and water. There were no plants, no animals, and no people. When the gods looked at the earth to see what they had made, they were unhappy.

"The earth is bare," they said. "Let us make life on the earth. Then we will be happy." So they made plants and animals. Now the earth was green and beautiful. The animals made a happy noise that reached all the way up to the gods. They mooed, barked, hissed, and roared, each one speaking in its own voice. The gods looked down and saw that the earth was a better place. But still they were not quite happy.

"The animals cannot speak our names. No one can honor us," the gods said. "Let us make people. We will teach them to speak our names and honor us. Then we will be happy."

So the gods tried to make people. First they made people of mud. But the mud people washed away in the rain. Then the gods carved people from wood. But the wooden people could not learn. The gods did not know what to do.

"Let us ask the animals," they thought. "They may be able to help us make people."

The animals were very wise. They knew the secrets of the forests and the rivers. So they took the gods into the forest and showed them a magic plant. The gods took the leaves of the magic plant and made them into men and women. As soon as the people were made, they began to speak the names of the gods. The gods were happy at last, and the people honored the gods for many years.

Think About It

Pretend you are making your own world. What are the three most important things you would put in it? Why?

12

Name _____

How People Were Made—
A South American Legend

Main Idea

1. What is the main idea of this story?

_____ The animals were smarter than the gods.

_____ The gods were happy when they made plants and animals.

_____ The animals helped the gods make people.

Sequencing

2. Number the events below in the order that they happened.

_____ The gods made people from the leaves of a magic tree.

_____ The gods made plants and animals.

_____ The gods made the earth of rock and water.

_____ The gods made people from mud.

Reading for Details

3. Use the clues to answer the questions.

Who made the earth? (paragraph 1) _____

What kinds of noises did the animals make? (paragraph 2)_____

_____

Where did the animals take the gods? (paragraph 6)_____

When did the people begin to speak? (paragraph 6)_____

_____

Why did the gods make people? (paragraph 3) _____

_____

Reading for Understanding

4. Write **happy** or **unhappy**.

When the gods made the earth of rock and water, they were _____

When the gods made plants and animals on Earth, they were _____

When the animals could not speak the gods names, the gods were _____

When the people began to speak the gods names, the gods were _____

Tony Beaver and the Watermelons

People in the state of West Virginia tell a story about a man named Tony Beaver. Tony was bigger and stronger than anyone else for miles around. He was taller than a house, and people could hide in the prints his shoes made in the mud. Tony loved to travel, and he loved to talk. Most of all, Tony loved to eat. But finding food for all those big meals was hard. So Tony decided to become a farmer and grow his own food.

Tony's favorite food was watermelon, so he bought some land and planted watermelon seeds. He hoed and weeded and worked in the fields every day. Soon the watermelons began to grow. They grew and grew, until by harvest time those watermelons were as big as barns. Tony had to build a special king-size wagon to haul them to market. But only one melon at a time would fit in the wagon. So Tony began the job of taking them to market one at a time.

Tony heaved the first melon into the wagon. The oxen hitched to the wagon pulled and tugged, and the wagon began to roll down the road toward the river. Everything was fine until they came to the first curve in the road. Then the wagon hit a rock, and the watermelon bounced off the wagon. Down the bank to the river rolled the giant melon with Tony running behind it. The melon splashed into the river, and Tony jumped in after it before he remembered he couldn't swim! But he was saved by his watermelon. The melon broke as it hit the water, so Tony just climbed up on a seed and paddled to shore.

Tony knew he would never get his crop to market, and he began to get restless. He decided to move on, and the last anyone knew, he was headed for Ohio.

Think About It
This story is called a tall tale. That means it is **exaggerated**. Write a tall tale about someone you know.

Name _____

Tony Beaver and the Watermelons

Main Idea
1. This story is about

_____ a farmer who couldn't get his watermelons to market.

_____ a man who loved to eat.

_____ a man who couldn't swim.

Sequencing
2. Number the events below in the order that they happened.

_____ He hoed and weeded and worked in the fields.

_____ The watermelons grew to be as big as barns.

_____ Tony tried to take the watermelons to market.

_____ Tony bought some land and planted watermelon seeds.

Reading for Details
3. Use the clues to answer the questions.

Who tells the story about Tony? (paragraph 1) _____

Where could people hide? (paragraph 1) _____

What was Tony taller than? (paragraph 1) _____

Why did Tony decide to become a farmer? (paragraph 1) _____

When were the watermelons as big as barns? (paragraph 2) _____

Reading for Understanding
4. Check the best answer(s).

What do you think Tony might do when he gets to Ohio?

_____ become a farmer again

_____ build a house on a straight road

_____ learn to swim

How the Chipmunk Got His Stripes

The Indians say that a long time ago, the chipmunk had no stripes on his back. His coat was dull brown, and he was not handsome like the squirrels. In fact, they laughed at him because he was so plain.

"Look at my bushy tail," said the red squirrel. "Don't you wish you had a tail like mine?"

"Look at my shiny coat," chirped the black squirrel. "Don't you wish you were beautiful like me?" The squirrels wouldn't even share the chestnuts they had stored, even though they had many.

So the chipmunk crept away into the forest to hide, never looking where he was going. He was so sad and hungry that he did not see a great bear sneak up on him. Suddenly he found himself trapped in the bear's paws!

"I will eat you now," growled the bear.

The chipmunk thought fast. "Before you eat me, let me sing and dance one last time," he pleaded.

The bear agreed. The chipmunk began to sing and dance. But out of the corner of his eye, he saw a hole to hide in. Quick as a flash, he ran toward it! But he was not fast enough. The bear's claws came down on his back. He twisted and wriggled, and at last he was free. He darted into the hole and was safe! But the marks of the bear's claws stayed on his back and became stripes.

When the squirrels saw the chipmunk again, they were surprised. "Why, you are so handsome," said the black squirrel. "We will make you king of the animals. Please take some of my nuts as a gift."

Now the chipmunk was happy. He had all the nuts he could eat, and the animals never laughed at him again.

Think About It

Write about a time either you or a friend was teased. How did it feel? What did you do?

Name _____

How the Chipmunk
Got His Stripes

Main Idea

1. Choose another title for this story.

_____ The Great Bear

_____ The Selfish Squirrels

_____ How the Bear Helped the
Chipmunk

Sequencing

2. Number the events below in the order that they happened.

_____ The squirrels laughed at the chipmunk.

_____ A bear clawed the chipmunk's back.

_____ The chipmunk crept away into the forest.

_____ The claw marks became stripes.

_____ The squirrels made the chipmunk king of the animals.

Reading for Details

3. Use the clues to answer the questions.

Who told this story a long time ago? (paragraph 1) _____

What wouldn't the squirrels share? (paragraph 3) _____

Where did the chipmunk run for safety? (paragraph 7) _____

Why was the chipmunk happy in the end? (paragraph 9) _____

_____

Reading for Understanding

4. Write the correct word or phrase.

I was sad and hungry when _____.

I was scared when _____.

I thought fast when _____.

The Unicorn

No one ever really saw a unicorn. But for many years, people told stories about this strange animal. They said the unicorn had a body like a horse, a tail like a lion, and a beard like a goat. But the unicorn got its name from its one horn that grew out of the middle of its forehead.

People believed the unicorn was a shy animal that lived in the middle of dark forests. It tried to stay away from people and other animals. But finding a unicorn was supposed to bring good luck. And its horn was supposed to have the power to find poison and cure sickness. So, long ago, people hunted unicorns. The hunters rode their horses into the forests, bringing their dogs to find the unicorn's trail. If they thought they saw a unicorn, the hunters chased it as fast as they could through the forest. But no matter how fast they rode, the unicorn ran faster. It knew all the secrets of the forest, so it could hide until the hunters went away. No hunter ever chased a unicorn and caught it.

There was only one way to catch a unicorn. A beautiful girl had to go into the forest. She would walk until she came to a pond. If she sat down by the pond, people said, a unicorn would come. The unicorn would see the girl and would fall in love with her. Very gently, it would lay its head on her lap. Then the girl could lead the unicorn out of the forest. It would follow her wherever she went, and she could keep it as a pet.

The Unicorn

Main Idea

1. Choose another title for this story.

_____ A Strange and Magical Animal

_____ A Beautiful Girl in the Forest

_____ How to Hunt a Unicorn

Sequencing

2. Number the events below in order.

_____ She would walk until she came to a pond.

_____ The unicorn would see the girl and fall in love with her.

_____ If she sat down by the pond, a unicorn would come.

_____ A beautiful girl would go into the forest.

_____ The unicorn would lay its head on her lap.

Reading for Details

3. Use the clues to answer the questions.

Who saw a unicorn? (paragraph 1)_____

What gave the unicorn its name? (paragraph 1) _____

Why did people hunt unicorns? (paragraph 2) _____

_____

Where did people go to hunt the unicorn? (paragraph 2) _____

When would the unicorn fall in love with the girl? (paragraph 3)_____

_____

Reading for Understanding

4. Why did I let the beautiful girl catch me?

_____ She gave me food.

_____ She gave me a place to live.

_____ She was kind and gentle to me.

The Story of Arachne

Long ago in a far country lived a young woman named Arachne. She was not rich or beautiful. But she had one great skill. She wove the most beautiful cloth anyone had ever seen. Everyone in Arachne's village talked about her wonderful cloth, and soon she became famous. But as she became more famous, she became more and more proud.

"No one else can weave as well as I can," she boasted. "Not even the goddess Minerva could make anything so lovely and fine."

Now Minerva wove the cloth for all the gods. She was proud of her weaving too and thought that no human could ever match her work. Soon Arachne's words reached Minerva's ears, and she became angry.

"So the human woman thinks she is better than I!" Minerva said. "We will see." So Minerva searched until she found Arachne's house. "So you think you are a fine weaver?" called Minerva. "Let us both weave a length of cloth. We will see whose cloth is more beautiful!"

Arachne agreed. She set up two looms, and she and Minerva went to work. The goddess wove cloth of all the colors of the rainbow. It sparkled in the sun and floated on the breeze like a butterfly. But Arachne wove cloth that looked like gold and jewels. It dazzled the eyes of anyone who looked at it. When Minerva looked at Arachne's cloth, she knew that Arachne could weave as well as any goddess.

Minerva flew into a rage. She took out a jar of magic water and sprinkled it on Arachne. At once Arachne began to change. She shrank until she became a tiny brown spider. Arachne would never boast again, but she would spend all her life as a weaver of fine webs.

Arachne is pronounced ä rak'nē.

20

The Story of Arachne

Main Idea

1. Long ago people made up myths to explain why things happened. What does this story explain?

_____ why cloth is woven

_____ why Arachne was not rich and beautiful

_____ why brown spiders weave fine webs

Sequencing

2. Number the events below in the order that they happened.

_____ Arachne wove a cloth that looked like gold and jewels.

_____ Arachne shrank until she became a tiny brown spider.

_____ Minerva sprinkled magic water on Arachne.

_____ Minerva challenged Arachne to a contest.

_____ Minerva saw that Arachne's cloth was as good as hers.

Reading for Details

3. Use the clues to answer the questions.

Where did Minerva find Arachne? (paragraph 4) _____

Who agreed to the weaving contest? (paragraph 5) _____

What did Minerva do when Arachne won the contest? (paragraph 6) _____

_____

When did Arachne begin to shrink? (paragraph 6) _____

_____

Reading for Understanding

4. Scan paragraph 5 and answer these questions.

What phrases are used to describe the cloth that the goddess wove? _____

_____

What phrases are used to describe the cloth that Arachne wove? _____

_____

Draw a picture of each piece of cloth.

The Wise Men and the Sensible Man

Long ago four men lived in a village in India. Three of the men read books and studied magic. Everyone thought they were great and wise men. The fourth man, whose name was Hari, knew no magic and did not spend his time studying, so none of the villagers listened to him. But this man had a great deal of sense.

One day, the four men went for a walk outside the village. As they walked, one of the men said to Hari, "Common sense is not useful. It will never make you rich or famous. You should study and learn magic like us."

Hari said nothing. He just walked along, looking at the trees. Soon the four men came to the bones of a dead animal. One of the men cried, "Now we can show Hari how wonderful it is to study magic. We can use our magic to bring this animal back to life." The other two magicians eagerly agreed. They decided that one man would put together the skeleton. Then the next man would make the flesh and skin, and the third man would give the animal life.

"Don't do this foolish thing," warned Hari. "Can't you see that these are the bones of a lion? If you bring it back to life, it will kill us."

But the men only laughed at Hari. The first man waved his hand and the skeleton stood up. The second man said a magic word, and the skeleton became a lion. Hari quickly climbed the nearest tree. The third man struck his walking stick on the ground, and the lion came to life. He pounced on the three wise men and gobbled them down in a flash.

And what happened to Hari? He waited until the lion was gone and then went home.

Hari is pronounced hahr′ee.

Name _____

The Wise Men and the Sensible Man

Main Idea
1. This story tells about

_____ a man whose life was saved because he was both smart and sensible.

_____ four men who took a walk.

_____ bones that came alive.

Sequencing
2. Number the events in the order that they happened.

_____ The wise men made the bones come alive.

_____ The four men went for a walk.

_____ Hari went home alive.

_____ The men came upon the bones of a lion.

Reading for Details
3. Use the clues to answer the questions.

Who didn't the villagers listen to? (paragraph 1) _____

Where did the men go on their walk? (paragraph 2) _____

_____

What did the men find on their walk? (paragraph 3) _____

Why did Hari tell the other men not to be foolish? (paragraph 4) _____

_____

When did Hari go home? (paragraph 6) _____

Reading for Understanding
4. To have common sense means to have

_____ lots of money.

_____ ordinary judgement.

_____ good judgement.

To be wise means

_____ having information.

_____ being old.

_____ having a big head.

The First Incas

Thousands of years ago, the people who lived in the Andes Mountains of South America were poor and miserable. They had no art and no skills to make tools. Worst of all, the tribes could not live in peace, and the people were always at war.

From their home in the sky, the sun god and the moon goddess watched. They felt sorry for the miserable people. "These people are grateful to us for the light we give them," said the sun god. "Let us send our son and daughter to teach them to live better. Then they can be happy."

The moon goddess agreed, but she was sad. The son and daughter were sad to leave their home too, but they were proud that they could help the people of the earth. They went down to earth by a lake and stayed there alone until they were old enough to help the people. Then the sun and moon's son called the people, and they came to the lake to hear him.

"My sister and I are children of the sun and moon, and we have come to help you," he declared. "You people are poor and miserable because you are always fighting each other. You do not think, so you are destroying the earth. What would happen if the sun and moon fought? They would destroy themselves and you too. We will teach you to live in peace like our father and mother."

The people were very grateful that the sun and moon had sent their children to help them, and they asked the children to be their king and queen. The people learned to weave cloth and to build houses. And most important, they learned to live in peace, and made one nation. They called themselves Incas, meaning "king's tribe," and for a long time they were a great people.

Think About It

How would you teach people to live in peace? Think of three things that are necessary for peace and tell why.

Name _____

The First Incas

Main Idea

1. Choose another title for this story.

_____ The Sun God and the Moon Goddess

_____ A Story About the Andes Mountains

_____ How Peace Came to the Incas

Sequencing

2. Number the events in the order that they happened.

_____ The sun god and the moon goddess felt sorry for the miserable people.

_____ The people lived in peace, made one nation, and called themselves the Incas.

_____ Thousands of years ago, people who lived in the Andes Mountains of South America were poor and miserable.

_____ The sun god and the moon goddess sent their children to help the people.

Reading for Details

3. Use the clues to answer the questions.

Where did the sun god and the moon goddess live? (paragraph 2)_____

_____

When did the son and daughter start to help the people? (paragraph 3)_____

_____

Why did the son think the people were miserable? (paragraph 4)_____

_____

What does "Incas" mean? (paragraph 5)_____

Reading for Understanding

4. Match the characters with the best adjective for each one by writing the correct letter.

a. Sun God   _____ peaceful

b. Son   _____ proud

c. Moon Goddess   _____ generous

d. Incas   _____ sad

The Knockers of Cornwall

The men who mine tin in Cornwall, England are serious people. They have no time for foolishness. But for hundreds of years, miners have said that "knockers," little goblins with funny faces, live in the mines.

Although some goblins are evil, the knockers like people. They enjoy helping the human miners as they work. The miners like the knockers too. When the miners hear the knocking and tapping sounds the knockers make with their hammers, they know there is ore nearby. Many miners have been ready to give up on a mine when the strange sounds have led them to a great vein of tin.

But in return for helping the miners, the knockers demand to be paid. They don't want money or gold. Each miner must leave a little bit of his dinner behind for them. Any miner who forgets, and eats all of his meal, makes the knockers angry, and then they bring him bad luck. Knockers don't like whistling or swearing either. Miners who forget and start whistling a tune as they work, find themselves showered with little stones that the knockers throw when they are angry.

Knockers, unlike most fairies and goblins, don't mind being seen. In fact, they love to tease the miners by popping out at them. They make ugly faces to frighten miners who are working in the dark. Sometimes they even come out of the mines at night to dance in the hills in the countryside. Then they dress up in old-fashioned red suits and wear yellow scarves around their heads. The bells on their arms and legs jingle as they dance wildly to the music that no one else can hear. Then, when morning comes, they hop back down into the mines to tease the miners again.

Name _____

The Knockers of Cornwall

Main Idea

1. Choose the main idea of paragraph 4.

_____ The knockers' bells jingle.

_____ The knockers love to tease the miners.

_____ The knockers dance at night.

Sequencing

2. Number the events in the order you learned about them.

_____ The miners give the knockers food.

_____ The knockers knock and tap by veins of metal.

_____ The knockers want to get paid.

_____ The miners find the veins of tin.

Reading for Details

3. Use the clues to answer the questions.

Who said that knockers live in mines? (paragraph 1)_____

_____

Where are the mines located? (paragraph 1) _____

When do the miners know there is ore nearby? (paragraph 2)_____

_____

What do the knockers demand for payment? (paragraph 3)_____

Why do the knockers throw stones? (paragraph 3) _____

_____

Reading for Understanding

4. We have things that we like and do not like. Put them in the right column.

people, helping, money, whistling, music, red suits, food, gold, teasing, bells dancing, yellow scarves, swearing

like	do not like

Selling the Sheepskin

Many years ago, an old man lived in a cottage with his only son. As the boy grew up, he began to think he was wiser than his father. So to test him, the father gave him a sheepskin and said, "Take this skin to the market. Don't come back home until you can bring me both the skin and the money someone paid you for it."

The boy set off down the road until he came to the market. Everyone he met asked to buy his fine sheepskin. But when the people found out he wanted to keep the skin and take the money for it too, they laughed at him. As it grew later and later, the boy grew tired and hungry. But he was ashamed to go home. Finally he gave up trying to sell the sheepskin. Instead, he watched a magician doing tricks in the marketplace. When everyone else had gone, he told the magician his problem.

"On your way home, say 'good morrow' to the first woman you meet," the magician told him. "You will have good luck."

So the boy walked along the road home. Before long, he came to a girl washing clothes by a stream. "Good morrow," said the boy.

"That is a fine sheepskin you have," the girl replied. "Give it to me." The girl took the skin and pulled off all the wool. Then she paid the boy for the wool and gave the skin back to him.

When the boy reached home, he told his father about the girl at the stream. His father exclaimed, "Find that wise girl again, for she is the one you shall marry!" So the boy searched the countryside until he found her, and they were married the next day.

Name _____

Selling the Sheepskin

Main Idea

1. Choose another title for this story.

_____ The Trip to the Market

_____ A Wise Father

_____ A Test for a Son

Sequencing

2. Number the events in the order that they happened.

_____ The boy told the magician his problem.

_____ The boy was ashamed to go home.

_____ The boy took the sheepskin to the market to sell.

_____ People in the market laughed at the boy.

Reading for Details

3. Use the clues to answer the questions.

When did the story take place? (paragraph 1) _____

_____

Why did the boy go to the market? (paragraph 1) _____

_____

Who told the boy how to solve his problem? (paragraph 3) _____

_____

What did the girl pay for? (paragraph 5) _____

_____

Where did the boy search for the girl? (paragraph 6) _____

_____

Reading for Understanding

4. Check the best answer.

The test showed that

_____ the boy was wiser than his father.

_____ the father was wiser than the boy.

_____ the magician was wiser than both the father and the boy.

_____ the girl was wisest of all.

The Indian Girl and the Serpent God

Once a beautiful Indian girl lived with her family in a Pueblo village. Though she was good and lovely, she had one strange habit. She spent all her time washing her clothes in the stream near the village. But in this stream there lived the snake god, and he became angry at the girl for dirtying his stream.

One day, when the girl went to the stream, the snake god rose up out of the water. He was a terrible serpent with fangs and shiny scales. "You have used my sacred water for yourself," he hissed. "Now you belong to me and must come with me to my home in the sea."

The girl was terrified, but she knew she must obey. She put on her best clothes and jewelry, and the great snake lay his huge head on her shoulder. Then they started out. The snake pushed her to show her the way.

The girl walked along the river and over the mountains. For days they traveled, and the girl grew tired and hungry. But the snake kept his head on her shoulder, so she moved on.

"Let us speak to each other. Are you tired?" the snake whispered. But the girl did not answer.

"Are you weary?" he asked again. The girl thought the voice sounded different this time.

"Why don't you look up?" said a kind voice. And when the girl finally did lift her eyes, she saw a handsome man. "I am the snake who traveled with you. See, here is my old coat." And he pulled the snake scales from under his cloak.

The girl forgot she had been sad. She gladly followed the young man under the sea and lived with him forever.

30

The Indian Girl and the Serpent God

Main Idea

1. This story tells about

_____ an Indian girl who meets a handsome man.

_____ an Indian girl with a strange habit.

_____ a serpent god who is unhappy.

Sequencing

2. Number the events in the order that they happened.

_____ The serpent god said that the girl had to go with him.

_____ The serpent god became a handsome young man.

_____ The girl went to the stream to wash clothes.

_____ The girl followed the young man under the water.

Reading for Details

3. Use the clues to answer the questions.

Who did the Indian girl live with? (paragraph 1) _____

Where did the Indian girl wash her clothes? (paragraph 1) _____

When did the snake god come out of the water? (paragraph 2) _____

_____

What did the Indian girl wear on her journey? (paragraph 3) _____

_____

Why did the Indian girl forget she was sad? (paragraph 8) _____

_____

Reading for Understanding

4. For each adjective listed, write the letter of the character it describes.

a. Indian girl

b. Serpent god

c. Young man

_____ beautiful   _____ lovely

_____ terrified   _____ sad

_____ handsome   _____ angry

_____ terrible   _____ kind

_____ good   _____ glad

_____ hungry

Phaeton and the Chariot of the Sun

Phaeton was a proud young man who lived in Greece when the world was still young. Although he lived on earth, Phaeton was the son of Apollo, the sun god. One day, Phaeton climbed to the top of Mount Olympus where the gods lived. Apollo was delighted to see his son. He showed Phaeton the palaces of the gods, and then he took him to see the horses of the sun.

"These horses pull my sun chariot across the sky every day," said Apollo. "They are very wild, and so no one can drive them but me."

When he heard this, Phaeton begged Apollo to let him drive. At first Apollo said no. But Phaeton begged so hard that at last the god gave in.

"You must hold the reins tightly or the horses will run away," Apollo warned. "And follow the tracks across the sky. Do not turn off the path."

Phaeton eagerly climbed into the chariot. But the horses galloped off so fast that Phaeton lost his breath. He let the reins drop, and the horses left the path. First they climbed to the heavens and set the stars on fire. Then they plunged close to the earth. The lakes dried up and the oceans boiled. Where there had been forests, there was now desert. The horses ran wild across the sky, burning the earth and its people.

From Mount Olympus, the chief god Zeus watched the chariot. He could not let the earth burn, so, sadly, he struck Phaeton with a bolt of lightning and turned him into a shooting star. The fiery star plunged into the ocean and disappeared. And although Apollo mourned for his son, he knew that Phaeton's pride had caused his death.

Think About It
Think of three things that you are proud of doing. Tell why.

Phaeton is pronounced fā'ton.

Name _____

Phaeton and the Chariot of the Sun

Main Idea

1. Choose the main idea of paragraph 5.

_____ The lakes dried up.

_____ Phaeton could not control the horses.

_____ The horses left the path and burned the earth.

Sequencing

2. Number the events below in the order that they happened.

_____ Phaeton climbed Mt. Olympus to visit his father.

_____ Phaeton begged Apollo to let him drive the sun chariot.

_____ Zeus turned Phaeton into a shooting star.

_____ Apollo showed Phaeton the horses of the sun.

_____ Phaeton let the reins drop, and the horses left the path.

Reading for Details

3. Use the clues to answer the questions.

Where did Phaeton live? (paragraph 1)_____

What did Phaeton climb into?(paragraph 5)_____

When did the horses leave the path? (paragraph 5)_____

_____

Who was Zeus? (paragraph 6) _____

Why did Zeus turn Phaeton into a shooting star? (paragraph 6)_____

_____

Reading for Understanding

4. Check the best answer.

When Phaeton climbed into the chariot, he felt

_____ excited   _____ unsure   _____ scared

When Apollo first saw Phaeton, he felt

_____ indifferent   _____ sad   _____ joyful

How did Zeus feel about turning Phaeton into a shooting star?

_____ unconcerned   _____ happy   _____ sad

The Beginning of Good and Evil

The people who live in Norway and Sweden say that in the beginning, there was no world. In the north there was only frozen darkness, but in the south there was only burning fire. And where the hot steam of the south met the cold mist of the frozen north, there were huge blocks of ice.

One day, two giants slowly rose up out of these huge blocks of ice. One was a man named Ymir, who was the father of everything evil and ugly. The other giant was a man named Buri. Buri was the father of everything good and beautiful. Ymir hated Buri.

Buri and Ymir both had many children. These children continually fought each other in the land of ice. That is how the struggle between good and evil began.

This fighting even continued between their grandchildren. One of Buri's grandchildren, Odin, eventually killed Ymir and all of his family, except for two children who escaped to the land of frozen darkness. Unfortunately, these two children were as evil and ugly as Ymir. They made their home in the land of frozen darkness, and they and their children became the frost giants.

Odin became the father of the gods. He made the world for people to live in and called it Midgard. He also made a place for the gods and called it Asgard. And he joined the two places with a rainbow bridge called Bifrost.

But all was not peaceful. The frost giants became the enemies of the gods. They made trouble for the gods and the people whenever they could. Even to this day they continue to make trouble and try to destroy the rainbow bridge between Midgard and Asgard.

Think About It
Why do the frost giants try to destroy the rainbow bridge?

Ymir is pronounced ee mihr.′
Buri is pronounced behr′ee.
Odin is pronounced ō′din.

Name _____

The Beginning of Good and Evil

Main Idea

1. Choose another title for this story.

_____ A Story from Norway and Sweden

_____ The Struggle Between Good and Evil

_____ Two Frost Giants

Sequencing

2. Number the events in the order that they happened.

_____ Odin killed Ymir and most of his children.

_____ The frost giants tried to make trouble.

_____ Buri and Ymir came out of the ice.

_____ Odin made Midgard and Asgard.

_____ Buri and Ymir had many children.

Reading for Details

3. Use the clues to answer the questions.

Who said there was no world in the beginning? (paragraph 1) _____

_____

What was in the north? (paragraph 1) _____

Where was the burning fire? (paragraph 1) _____

Why did Odin make Midgard? (paragraph 5) _____

When did the frost giants make trouble for the people and the gods? (paragraph 6) _____

_____

Reading for Understanding

4. Write the letter in the correct space.

a. Odin _____ a rainbow bridge

b. Midgard _____ father of the gods

c. Asgard _____ the world

d. Bifrost _____ place for the gods

e. Ymir _____ father of everything good and beautiful

f. Buri _____ father of everything evil and ugly

The Story of Zan

On the island of Crete, the Great Earth Mother had a child whom she named Zan. The bees of the forest brought honey for little Zan, and the wild goats gave him milk. But children must have toys. So the five servants of the Great Earth Mother made toys for him, and each toy was made of a different kind of material. Zan played happily on the mountains with his toys and with the animals of the forest.

When he grew up into a strong, kind man, Zan wanted to reward his animal friends. So he made a law that the goats could roam wherever they wished on the mountains. He made hives for the bees to protect them from the cold winds and snow. Then Zan took the toys he had saved and hid them in a secret cave where they would be safe. He asked the bees to guard the cave.

One day three evil men climbed up the mountain to find treasure. They put on armor to protect themselves from the bees, and they crept through the bushes until they reached the mouth of the cave. The bees buzzed around to attack the men. But their armor protected the men and they went inside.

Suddenly Zan appeared in the cave. "Stop!" he shouted. "You have come here to rob and kill. I must let you live, for this is the cave of life. But from now on you will never be able to tell other people where my wonderful cave is."

As Zan finished speaking, the men turned into birds. One turned into a woodpecker, one became a thrush, and one became an owl. And even today, when the birds speak, no one can understand them.

The Story of Zan

Main Idea

1. Choose the main idea of paragraph 2.

_____ Zan became a strong, kind man and rewarded his animal friends.

_____ Zan put his toys in a secret cave.

_____ Zan made hives for the bees.

Sequencing

2. Number the events in the order that they happened.

_____ Animals gave gifts to Zan.

_____ The Earth Mother had a child named Zan.

_____ Zan rewarded his animal friends.

_____ Zan turned the men into birds.

_____ Three evil men tried to steal Zan's toys.

Reading for Details

3. Use the clues to answer the questions.

Where was Zan born? (paragraph 1) _____

Who gave the milk to Zan? (paragraph 1) _____

When did Zan reward his animal friends? (paragraph 2) _____

_____

Why did Zan let the evil men live? (paragraph 4) _____

_____

What did Zan turn the men into? (paragraph 5) _____

_____

Reading for Understanding

4. Long ago people made up stories to explain why things happened.

What does this story explain?

_____ why goats give milk

_____ why no one can understand birds

_____ why no one can be killed in the cave of life

The Loup-Garou

Many of us know the legends about werewolves – people who turn into wolves and do evil things. Among the French-speaking people of North America, werewolf legends have been told for hundreds of years. But in these stories, people could turn into many kinds of animals: wolves, bears, dogs, oxen, and even pigs. A person who could change himself into these animals was called a loup-garou, and people ran whenever they saw him. Many French mothers made their children behave by telling them the loup-garou would get them.

People became loup-garoux in several ways. Sometimes a witch would cast a spell on them. Other times, it was said, a person might make an agreement with the devil. He would say, "Devil, I engage myself to you." Then the devil would appear and give the man money, and in return the man would promise to be a loup-garou for six months.

No one could be sure who was a loup-garou. But sometimes a person might come to the door of a house and then suddenly disappear. Then the people living in the house knew that they had seen a loup-garou. They would shut all the doors and windows and even plug up the cracks, because they were afraid the loup-garou might throw bad magic into the house.

A loup-garou could trap its victim by getting in the way of the victim's feet while he was walking. The only way to escape a loup-garou was to stab it with a knife or something else sharp so it would bleed. As soon as a drop of blood fell, the animal skin would fall to the ground, and the person who had been a loup-garou would come out.

Loup-garou is pronounced loop gahr oo.
Loup-garoux is pronounced loop gahr oos.

The Loup-Garou

Main Idea

1. Choose another title for this story.

_____ How to Escape a Loup-Garou's Trap

_____ A Witch's Spell

_____ The French Werewolf

Sequencing

2. Number the events in the order that they happened.

_____ A drop of blood would fall.

_____ A loup-garou would trap its victim.

_____ The animal skin would fall to the ground.

_____ To escape, the victim would cut the loup-garou.

_____ The person who had been a loup-garou would come out.

Reading for Details

3. Use the clues to answer the questions.

Who told the legends of the werewolves? (paragraph 1) _____

_____

Why did French mothers tell their children that a loup-garou might get them?

(paragraph 1) _____

What kind of animals can the people turn into? (paragraph 1) _____

_____

Where might the loup-garou throw bad magic? (paragraph 3) _____

_____

When would the animal skin fall to the ground? (paragraph 4) _____

_____

Reading for Understanding

4. Check the correct statements.

_____ I became a loup-garou by making an agreement with the devil.

_____ I have to work for a witch for six months.

_____ It is easy to get away from me.

_____ I trap a person by tripping him.

Tuwara and the Mosquitoes

The god Tuwara lived on a beautiful island in the Pacific Ocean. The island had fruit trees and flowers and high clear waterfalls. The people loved Tuwara because he was kind and wise. Life was perfect except for one thing. Each night, thousands of mosquitoes flew into the village, buzzing and biting the people.

Finally, the people begged Tuwara to get rid of the mosquitoes. He thought a long time. Then he sailed off to a nearby island. The king of the island welcomed Tuwara and gave a feast for him with music and dancing.

"This is a beautiful island and your people sing well," said Tuwara. "But on my island, there are little people who sing the sweetest song in the world. If you come with me, you can hear them."

The king agreed, and they sailed back to Tuwara's island. When night came, Tuwara took the king inside his hut. He whispered, "Hide under these cloths, for if the little people see you, they will run away." The king hid, and soon the mosquitoes came buzzing.

"That's the most wonderful singing I have ever heard!" exclaimed the king. "Could I take some of these people back to my island so they can sing for me?"

Tuwara smiled. The next morning, while the mosquitoes slept, he gathered them all into a bag. He gave the bag to the king and said, "Here are the little people. Take them to your island. But don't open the bag until you get home, or they will run away."

The king thanked Tuwara and sailed for home. From that day, Tuwara's island had no mosquitoes. But the king of the other island and his people were tortured by the little singers forever.

Tuwara is pronounced too wor´uh.

Name _____

Tuwara and the Mosquitoes

Main Idea
1. Choose another title for this story.

_____ The Little Singers

_____ An Island in the Pacific

_____ How the King Rid His Island of Mosquitoes

Sequencing
2. Number the events in the order that they happened.

_____ Tuwara gathered the mosquitoes in a bag.

_____ The people begged Tuwara to get rid of the mosquitoes.

_____ Tuwara gave the mosquitoes to the king.

_____ Tuwara invited the king to his island.

_____ Tuwara's island had no mosquitoes.

Reading for Details
3. Use the clues to answer the questions.

Why did the people love Tuwara? (paragraph 1)_____

_____

What did the mosquitoes do that bothered the people? (paragraph 1)_____

_____

Where did Tuwara go? (paragraph 2)_____

When did Tuwara take the king into the hut? (paragraph 4)_____

_____

Who were the little people? (paragraph 6)_____

Reading for Understanding
4. Choose another solution for Tuwara's problem.

_____ cast a spell on the mosquitoes so they would not be able to buzz or bite

_____ move his people to a different island

_____ gather the mosquitoes in a bag and sink it in the ocean

The Tiny Fliers

Did you ever see a tiny bird flying around some flowers in the summertime? Did its wings move so fast that you couldn't even see them? That little bird was a hummingbird, the smallest bird of all.

There are 320 different kinds of hummingbirds in the world, and they all live in North America or South America. The tiniest hummingbird is only as long as your finger! But its biggest cousin is almost as big as a robin. This giant hummingbird lives in South America. Most hummingbirds that live in the United States and Canada are about four inches or 10 cm long. They have feathers of many colors, and when they fly around the flowers, they look almost like flowers that have learned to fly. You may have seen a ruby-throated hummingbird, with its red throat and shiny green back, flying in a park or garden.

Flying is what hummingbirds do best. they even got their name from the sound they make when they fly. Their wings beat so fast that they make the air hum. A hummingbird must move its wings all the time when it is in the air. It can't glide on the air the way some birds can. But it can do two things that no other bird can do. It can fly in one place, like a helicopter, and it can fly backwards. So the hummingbird is king of the fliers.

Flying makes hummingbirds hungry. They spend all day drinking the juice, or nectar, from flowers. They make their long tongues into tubes and suck the nectar as you would suck juice through a straw. For snacks, they eat insects as they fly. Every day a hummingbird must eat sixty meals to give it energy to fly! So the little king of the fliers is king of the eaters too.

The Tiny Fliers

Main Idea

1. Choose another title for this story.

_____ Flying Flowers

_____ Sixty Meals a Day

_____ King of the Fliers

Sequencing

2. Number the events below in the order that they happen.

_____ They suck the nectar from flowers.

_____ Hummingbirds look for flowers.

_____ Flying makes hummingbirds hungry.

_____ They make their long tongues into tubes.

Reading for Details

3. Use the clues to answer these questions.

What is the smallest bird of all? (paragraph 1) _____

Where do all the different kinds of hummingbirds live? (paragraph 2) _____

_____

When do hummingbirds look just like flowers? (paragraph 2) _____

_____

Why do hummingbirds eat all the time? (paragraph 4) _____

_____

Reading for Understanding

4. Check the correct answer(s).

I am king of the fliers because

_____ I can hover and fly backwards.

_____ I can fly upside down.

I am king of the eaters because

_____ I can make my tongue work like a straw.

_____ I eat 60 meals a day.

I was named a hummingbird because

_____ my wings beat so fast that they make the air hum.

_____ I look like a flower.

The Big Bird with the Big Bill

An old rhyme goes, "A wonderful bird is a pelican; its bill will hold more than its belly can." The person who wrote that rhyme was right. A pelican has a big pouch under its bill. The pouch will hold more than three gallons of water, far more than a pelican can hold in its stomach.

North America is home for two kinds of pelicans. The white pelican lives around lakes in the western United States. The brown pelican lives near the ocean in California and around the Gulf of Mexico. Both kinds of pelicans are big birds. Whites weigh twenty pounds, or 9 kilograms, and are five feet, or 1.5 meters, long. Browns are smaller. They weigh only half as much as the whites and are a little shorter. Both pelicans eat fish. But they don't go fishing in the same way.

Brown pelicans like to fish alone. They fly over the water looking for fish far below. When they see a fish, they dive into the water and scoop it up in their bills.

White pelicans like to fish together. They also fly high above the water looking for fish. But when these pelicans find a group of fish, they land on the water. Then they form a half-circle and start beating their wings on the water. The frightened fish swim to the middle of the circle, and the pelicans start their tasty meal.

For a while it seemed that only one kind of pelican might be left. Almost all the brown pelicans died because of dirty, unsafe water in the Gulf of Mexico. But people began to clean up the water in time, and now the number of brown pelicans is growing again. So when you see this bird that carries its own shopping bag in its bill, remember that his bill really will hold more than his belly can!

Name _____

The Big Bird with the Big Bill

Main Idea

1. This story tells about

_____ an old rhyme.

_____ a dirty and unsafe Gulf of Mexico.

_____ two kinds of pelicans.

Sequencing

2. Number the events below in the order that they happen.

_____ When they see fish, they land on the water and form a half-circle.

_____ They beat their wings on the water to make the fish swim to the middle of the circle.

_____ They eat the fish.

_____ White pelicans fly together high above the water.

Reading for Details

3. Use the clues to answer these questions.

Who was right about the pelican? (paragraph 1)_____

What part of a pelican will hold three gallons of water? (paragraph 1) _____

Where is the home of pelicans? (paragraph 2) _____

When does a brown pelican dive into the water and scoop up a fish in its bill?

(paragraph 3) _____

Why did brown pelicans become endangered? (paragraph 5) _____

_____

Reading for Understanding

4. Put these phrases in the right column.

lives around lakes in the western United States, lives near the ocean and the Gulf of Mexico, weighs 20 pounds, 5 feet long, weighs 10 pounds, shorter than 5 feet, fishes alone, fishes together, beats wings and frightens fish into a circle, almost died out, bill can hold more than its belly

Brown Pelican _____   White Pelican _____

_____   _____

_____   _____

_____   _____

The Ice of Summer

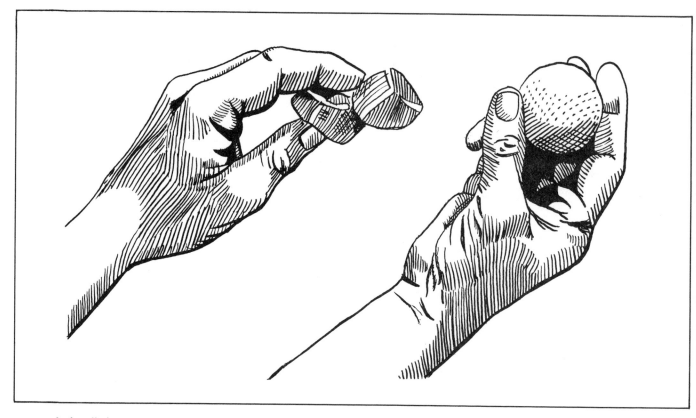

A hailstorm can be a terrible sight to see. So many hailstones may fall that the ground becomes as white as snow. As they fall, hailstones may break windows and flatten plants. They may even kill animals. They sound like thunder as they beat on the roofs of houses. Hailstones are balls of ice. But since hailstorms happen in the summer, where does the ice come from?

A hailstorm starts out as a rainstorm, and a hailstone starts out as a raindrop. Sometimes in the summer there is a layer of cold air just above the earth. When a raindrop falls through this cold air, it freezes. Before it can reach the ground, wind carries it up into warm air again. In the warm air, more raindrops stick to the frozen raindrop. When the frozen raindrop falls into the cold air again, the raindrops sticking to it freeze too. Now the frozen raindrop is bigger. If the wind carries the raindrop up again, it may collect more water in the warm air. Then it falls back into the cold air and freezes again. The raindrop may bounce back and forth between the warm air and the cold air many times. Each time it bounces, it gets bigger. Finally it is a ball of ice called a hailstone. When it is heavy enough, the hailstone falls to the ground. Some hailstones can weigh as much as a pound, and they do great damage. But most hailstones are much smaller and less harmful, although they can ruin your garden.

Hailstorms, with their winds and lightning, are exciting. But they can be dangerous too. So it's good that hailstorms only happen once in a while.

Name _____

The Ice of Summer

Main Idea

1. This story explains

_____ rainstorms.

_____ thunder and lightning.

_____ hailstorms.

Sequencing

2. Number the events below in the order that they happen.

_____ The hailstone becomes heavy and falls to the ground.

_____ When more raindrops freeze on the frozen raindrop, it gets bigger.

_____ A raindrop falls through cold air and freezes.

_____ Wind carries the frozen raindrop back up to the warm air.

Reading for Details

3. Use the clues to answer these questions.

What are hailstones? (paragraph 1) _____

What does a hailstone start out as? (paragraph 2) _____

Where is the layer of cold air found in the summer? (paragraph 2) _____

_____

When does the raindrop freeze? (paragraph 2) _____

_____

Why can hailstones do great damage? (paragraph 2) _____

_____

Reading for Understanding

4. Write yes or no in the blank.

A hailstorm can be described as

_____ deadly   _____ beautiful

_____ damaging   _____ terrible

_____ scary   _____ exciting

_____ harmful   _____ dangerous

Fiery Visitors from Outer Space

On the next clear summer night, look up into the sky. If you are lucky, you may see a "shooting star." Shooting stars streak across the dark sky, and then they fall to earth. They look just like stars falling down from the sky.

But shooting stars are not stars at all. The real name for a shooting star is "meteor." There are millions of meteors out in space. They are pieces of rock and metal. Some of them come from comets, but nobody knows where others come from. When they are in space, meteors do not glow. In fact, we can't see them at all. But when a meteor comes close to the earth, it starts to fall toward the earth. As it passes through the air, it gets very hot. It starts to glow, and finally it begins to burn. We see the burning meteor as a shooting star.

Sometimes meteors travel by themselves in space. But many meteors travel in groups called swarms. The swarms have orbits like planets have. They pass close to the earth every year. A famous swarm is the Perseid swarm. It passes close to the earth in summer, usually in August. Each year a few meteors from the Perseid swarm fall to earth, so August is a good month to watch for shooting stars.

Most meteors are small, so they burn up before they reach the ground. But some meteors are large. They crash into the earth and are buried in the ground. Once a meteor reaches the earth, we call it a meteorite. The biggest meteorite, which weighs seventy tons, landed in Africa.

Next time you see a shooting star, you'll know it is not really a star. But keep looking at the sky, for there may be other meteors following it soon.

Name _____

Fiery Visitors from Outer Space

Main Idea
1. Choose another title for this story.

_____ Travel in Space

_____ Shooting Stars

_____ A Meteorite in Africa

Sequencing
2. Number the events below in the order that they happen.

_____ We see a "shooting star."

_____ As it passes through the air, it gets very hot.

_____ It starts to glow and begins to burn.

_____ A meteor comes close to the earth and starts to fall.

Reading for Details
3. Use the clues to answer these questions.

When might you see a meteor? (paragraph 1) _____

_____

What are meteors made of? (paragraph 2) _____

Where do some meteors come from? (paragraph 2) _____

When don't meteors glow? (paragraph 2) _____

Why do meteors glow when they get close to earth? (paragraph 2) _____

_____

Reading for Understanding
4. Place the correct letter in the space.

_____ Meteor   a. a famous swarm of meteors

_____ Swarm   b. a meteor that has reached the earth

_____ Perseid   c. the real name for a shooting star

_____ Meteorite   d. a group of meteors

Giants of the Forest

Can you imagine a tree as tall as a football field is long? Can you imagine many of them standing so tall that you cannot see their tops? If you can, then you can imagine a redwood forest.

Redwoods are the tallest trees in the world. The tallest redwood is taller than a twenty-story building. It is so big around that six people holding hands could barely reach around it.

How do redwoods get so big? First, they live where the weather is just right for them. Redwood trees grow near the Pacific Ocean in the states of California and Oregon. They live in an area with hot, dry summers and warm, rainy winters. So they don't have to worry about the cold. Though they don't get much rain, fog comes in every day, and the trees get water from the fog. And redwoods are not hurt by pests. Redwoods have very thick bark, so insects can't hurt the inside of the trees.

Even fire does not hurt redwood trees. Redwoods have three ways to guard against forest fire. First, their bark must get very hot in order to burn. Next, the needles and branches, which burn more easily than the bark, are far up from the ground. Fire almost never reaches them. And because redwood branches keep the sunlight from getting to the forest floor, not many plants can grow under redwoods. So fires don't start easily in the forest.

It's a good thing redwoods are so healthy, for they take many years to grow. They grow so slowly because they don't get much rainfall. But they often live and keep growing for two thousand years! They are some of the oldest living things in the world.

Name _____

Giants of the Forest

Main Idea
1. Choose another title for the story.

_____ The Redwood Forest

_____ Fun in the Forest

_____ A Slow-Growing Tree

Sequencing
2. Number the events below in the order that you read about them.

_____ Fire does not hurt redwood trees.

_____ Redwood trees grow near the Pacific Ocean in California and Oregon.

_____ Trees get water from the fog.

_____ Insects cannot hurt redwoods.

Reading for Details
3. Use the clues to answer these questions.

What are the tallest trees in the world? (paragraph 2) _____

How big is the tallest redwood? (paragraph 2) _____

Where do redwood trees grow? (paragraph 3) _____

When does the fog come in? (paragraph 3) _____

Why can't insects hurt the inside of the redwood trees? (paragraph 3) _____

_____

Reading for Understanding
4. Check the correct answer(s).

Fires do not start easily in redwood forests because

_____ their bark must get very hot in order to burn.

_____ their needles and branches, which burn easily, are far up off the ground.

_____ not many plants grow under the redwoods.

_____ few people go into redwood forests.

The Florida Key Deer

If you live in the eastern United States or southeastern Canada, you have probably seen white-tailed deer. They roam in large herds in forests and grassy countryside from Canada to South America. In some places, there are so many that they anger farmers by eating crops and gardens. But their tiny cousins, the Florida Key deer, have not been so lucky. Forty years ago, there were almost none of these deer left at all.

The Florida Key deer look like ordinary white-tailed deer except for their size. Most white-tailed deer weigh 400 pounds or 181 kilograms and are more than a meter tall. But the biggest Key deer weigh much less and are only half as tall. These little deer live in pine forests and swamps on the islands south of Florida. These islands are called the Florida Keys and the deer are named for them.

A hundred years ago, hundreds of Key deer lived in the forests on the Keys. But then hunters discovered them. Groups of hunters would go into the forest and make noise to frighten the deer into the water. Then other hunters in boats would kill them. By 1947 less than forty little deer were left.

But then some of the people living on the Keys began to worry about the deer. They bought some land and used it as a shelter to protect the very last of the Key deer. Two years later, the United States government bought land in the Keys and formed the National Key Deer Refuge. Now the deer had eleven square miles of forest where they could live safely.

Luckily, the deer were saved in time. Once they had lived on only five small islands in the Keys, but by 1965 they had spread to eighteen islands. And today more than 400 Florida Key deer are alive because some people cared.

52

Name _____

The Florida Key Deer

Main Idea

1. Choose another title for this story.

_____ The Deer that Almost
         Disappeared

_____ The National Key Deer Refuge

_____ The Florida Keys

Sequencing

2. Number the events below in the order that they happened.

_____ Hunters killed the Key deer.

_____ The United States government bought land for a refuge.

_____ Some people bought land to use as a shelter.

_____ The Key deer spread from five islands to eighteen islands.

Reading for Details

3. Use the clues to answer these questions.

Who gets angry at the white-tailed deer for eating crops and gardens? (paragraph 1)

_____

What is the name of the white-tailed deer's cousin? (paragraph 1) _____

_____

Where are white-tailed deer found? (paragraph 1) _____

_____

When did lots of Key deer live in the forest on the Keys? (paragraph 3) _____

_____

Why were less than forty deer left by 1947? (paragraph 3) _____

_____

Reading for Understanding

4. Choose the topic for paragraph 2.

_____ an ordinary white-tailed deer

_____ the Florida Key deer

_____ what Florida Key deer eat

Tasting—A Team Effort

How many different kinds of things can you taste? You may think you can taste a hundred different flavors. Chocolate ice cream tastes different than vanilla ice cream, and potatoes taste different than carrots. But you can really taste only four different flavors with your tongue.

All over the tongue are little bumps called "taste buds" which taste the food you put in your mouth. There are four different kinds of taste buds. One kind, which is on the tip of the tongue, tastes sweet things. The second kind, at the back of the tongue, tastes bitter things. The third and fourth kinds, which lie on the sides of the tongue, taste salty and sour things. But if these are the only flavors the tongue can taste, why do so many foods taste different from each other?

When you think you are tasting most foods, you are really smelling them. You may have noticed that when you have a cold, you can't taste very well. But there is nothing wrong with your tongue. When you eat, some of the oils from the food rise into the air and you breathe them in. The oils land on small hairs inside your nose. The hairs send signals to the brain, and you smell the food. When you are eating, though, you think of the special smell as a taste. If your nose is stuffy, the food oils cannot get into your nose, so you cannot smell. You are left with only the four flavors your tongue can taste.

Tasting makes eating more fun. The tongue and the nose work together as a team to help you enjoy your food. Without this teamwork, eating would be a very dull business of the same old four flavors every day.

Name _____

Tasting — A Team Effort

Main Idea

1. Choose another title for this story.

_____ Eating With Gusto

_____ Why We Taste Food

_____ The Four Flavors

Sequencing

2. Number the events below in the order that they happen.

_____ You breathe the food oils in.

_____ The nose hairs send signals to the brain.

_____ The oils land on the small hairs inside your nose.

_____ You smell the food.

Reading forDetails

3. Use the clues to answer these questions.

Who can taste only four flavors? (paragraph 1) _____

What are the little bumps on your tongue called? (paragraph 2) _____

_____

Where do you taste sweet things on your tongue? (paragraph 2) _____

_____

When do you think of a special smell as taste? (paragraph 3) _____

_____

Why can't you taste food very well when you have a cold? (paragraph 3) _____

_____

Reading for Understanding

4. Choose the topic of the following paragraphs.

Paragraph 2	Paragraph 3
_____ bitter things	_____ why you can smell
_____ cherry pie	_____ why you can taste
_____ taste buds	_____ how you feel when you have a cold

The Baker's Friend

If you have ever watched someone bake bread, you know that the bread dough must "rest" for an hour or two before it is baked. In that time, magic seems to happen. The flat, gooey lump of dough grows into a light, spongy ball that fills the bowl. But it is yeast, not magic, that makes the bread light and airy.

Before the baker adds the yeast to bread dough, the yeast looks like a gray powder or, sometimes, a little gray block. But the yeast you see is really made of millions of tiny plants. They are not green, and they do not have leaves or flowers. If you could see a yeast plant under a microscope, it would look like a round gray pillow.

When the yeast plants are kept dry, they seem to be dead. But they are still alive, waiting for the food and water they need to grow. Bakers help the yeast plants grow by mixing them into the dough they are making. As soon as the water in the dough touches the yeast plants, they begin to use the flour and sugar in the dough for food. They grow bigger and make more yeast plants, so soon all the dough is filled with growing yeast. As they use food, the yeast plants give off alcohol and gas. The gas makes bubbles in the dough, and the dough rises.

When the baker puts a pan of bread into a hot oven to bake, the heat makes the gas bubbles even bigger, and the bread rises even more. The bread dough bakes into a fresh, light loaf of bread, full of the gas bubbles the yeast plants have made.

Many bakers are proud of their light, tasty bread. But they could never manage at all without their hardworking friends, the yeast plants.

Name _____

The Baker's Friend

Main Idea

1. This story explains

_____ how yeast makes bread rise.

_____ why a baker bakes bread.

_____ where yeast plants come from.

Sequencing

2. Number the events below in the order that they happen.

_____ The yeast plants use the flour and sugar for food.

_____ The yeast plants give off alcohol and gas as they grow.

_____ Bakers add yeast to bread dough.

_____ The bread dough is baked into a fresh, light loaf of bread.

Reading for Details

3. Use the clues to answer these questions.

Who adds the yeast to the bread? (paragraph 2) _____

What is yeast? (paragraph 2) _____

What does a yeast plant look like under a microscope? (paragraph 2) _____

_____

When do yeast plants seem to be dead? (paragraph 3) _____

_____

Why are many bakers proud? (paragraph 5) _____

_____

Reading for Understanding

4. Circle yes or no.

The bubbles from the alcohol and gas that yeast gives off make the bread rise.	Yes	No
When the baker puts the pan of bread into the hot oven to bake, the gas bubbles get smaller.	Yes	No
The bread dough bakes into a stale, hard lump of bread.	Yes	No
Yeast is not green.	Yes	No
Yeast does not have leaves or flowers.	Yes	No

Quiet! A Fish May Be Listening

Perhaps you have gone fishing with a friend. If you were careless and made noise, your friend might have said, "Be quiet! You'll scare the fish!" Did you believe it? You should have because fish can hear very well.

Fish do not have any ears on the outside of their bodies as most animals do. Instead, the ears of a fish are inside its head, just behind the eyes. And fish do not hear the same way other animals hear. First, the sound enters a special bag in the fish's body. This bag is called the air bladder. Then the air bladder sends the sound to a box in the fish's ear. The box is full of little stones. The stones are called "otoliths," and they move when sound comes into the box. When the otoliths move, the fish hears the sound.

The fish's ears have another job too. They help the fish stay right-side up in the water. In the fish's ear are three hollow bones shaped like horseshoes. They are filled with liquid. When the fish moves, the liquid moves inside the bones. Then the fish's brain knows that the fish is right-side up in the water. If something was wrong with these bones, the fish might swim on its side, or even upside down!

Fish also have a special organ that no other animal has. It is called the "lateral line." The lateral line is a row of scales on the fish's side. When water waves move against the lateral line, the line tells the fish how fast the water is moving and where the waves came from. Because sound makes waves in the water, the lateral line helps the fish hear too.

So, next time you're fishing, be careful not to splash. The clever fish will hear you and swim away.

Name _____

Quiet! A Fish
May Be Listening

Main Idea
1. Choose another title for this story.
_____ The Lateral Line of a Fish
_____ The Careful Fisherman
_____ Fish Hearing

Sequencing
2. Number the events below in the order that they happen.
_____ The air bladder sends the sound to a box in the fish's ear.
_____ When the otoliths move, the fish hears the sound.
_____ The otoliths move when the sound enters the box.
_____ The sound enters the air bladder.

Reading for Details
3. Use the clues to answer these questions.

Who might say "Be quiet!" while you are fishing? (paragraph 1) _____

_____

What is the name of the special bag inside the fish's body? (paragraph 2) _____

_____

Where are the otoliths? (paragraph 2) _____

When do the otoliths move? (paragraph 2) _____

_____

Why is it important not to splash when you are fishing? (paragraph 5) _____

_____

Reading for Understanding
4. Circle the correct answer.

My ears have (one, two) jobs.

My ears keep me (upright, upside down) in the water.

My ears have (two, three) hollow bones shaped like horseshoes in them.

My other special organ is called the (lateral line, longitunal line) which helps me to hear too.

11/3/01

Your Personal Mark

Have you ever felt like you were just the same as everybody else? The next time you feel that way, take a look at your finger. Even if you are a twin, you have something nobody else has. You have your own special fingerprints. What causes fingerprints, and why are they different for each person?

To find out, you must know about the skin. The skin is made up of two layers: a thick bottom layer and a very thin top layer. On most of the body, the top layer lies smoothly on the bottom layer. But on the fingertips, the top and bottom layers fit together very tightly. The top layer of skin is so tight that it makes the bottom layer wrinkle. These wrinkles are "fingerprints."

Monkeys and apes have fingerprints too. The wrinkles on the fingers of monkeys and apes form straight rows across the fingers. But all the straight rows are much alike, so apes don't have their own special fingerprints.

The wrinkles on people's fingers form patterns of loops and spirals on the fingertips. The exact pattern of the loops and spaces between loops is a little different for every person in the world, so no two people have the same fingerprints. Even more surprising, people's fingerprints stay the same all their lives. The fingerprints you were born with are the very same ones you will have when you are old.

Fingerprints help the police to catch criminals and find missing people. But they are important for you too. If you ever feel lost in a crowd, look at your finger and remember that you are special.

Name _____

Your Personal Mark

Main Idea
1. Choose another title for this story.

_____ Your Fingerprints

_____ Your Skin

_____ Monkeys and Apes

Sequencing
2. Number the events below in the order that you read about them.

_____ Fingerprints help police catch criminals.

_____ No two people have the same pattern of fingerprints.

_____ Wrinkles on people's fingers form patterns of loops and spirals.

_____ Fingerprints stay the same all of a person's life.

Reading for Details
3. Use the clues to answer these questions.

Who uses fingerprints to catch criminals and find missing people? (paragraph 5) _____

_____

What causes fingerprints? (paragraph 2) _____

_____

Where are your fingerprints located? (paragraph 2) _____

_____

When do your fingerprints change? (paragraph 4) _____

Why are fingerprints different for each person? (paragraph 4) _____

_____

Reading for Understanding
4. You have learned many things about fingerprints. Check the things that are correct.

_____ Fingerprints are special.

_____ Twins have the same fingerprints.

_____ The top layer of skin on the fingertips is so tight that it makes the bottom layer wrinkle.

_____ Monkeys and apes have their own fingerprints.

_____ The wrinkles are the fingerprints.

Mysterious Sunspots

In 1610, a man named Galileo invented the telescope so he could see the stars. But one day he looked through his telescope at the sun and saw something that surprised him. The sun was not a smooth yellow ball. Instead, Galileo saw large black spots on the sun. He never could explain what they were, although he watched them often. And sunspots are almost as much a mystery now as in Galileo's time.

Astronomers, people who study stars and planets, think that sunspots are huge storms on the sun. But the storms are not made up of clouds and rain. They are whirlwinds of hot gases and electrical particles. They shoot up from the sun for thousands of miles, then sink back again. As the gases shoot out from the sun, they cool off and do not glow, so they look black against the bright sun.

Even though they are millions of miles away, sunspots affect the earth. The Aurora Borealis, or Northern Lights, which are waves of light that flicker across the night sky, are brighter when there are many sunspots. The Aurora can always be seen around the North Pole, but during sunspot activity, even people in the United States can see the Aurora. Sunspots can change the weather, too, by increasing the amount of ozone in the air. The thicker ozone blanket keeps out the sunlight, so the weather becomes cooler. Finally, because sunspots are electrical, they can interfere with radio signals, causing static and crackling that makes a radio hard to hear.

Astronomers are very curious about sunspots. And maybe one day they will solve the mystery of why sunspots happen.

Name _____

Mysterious Sunspots

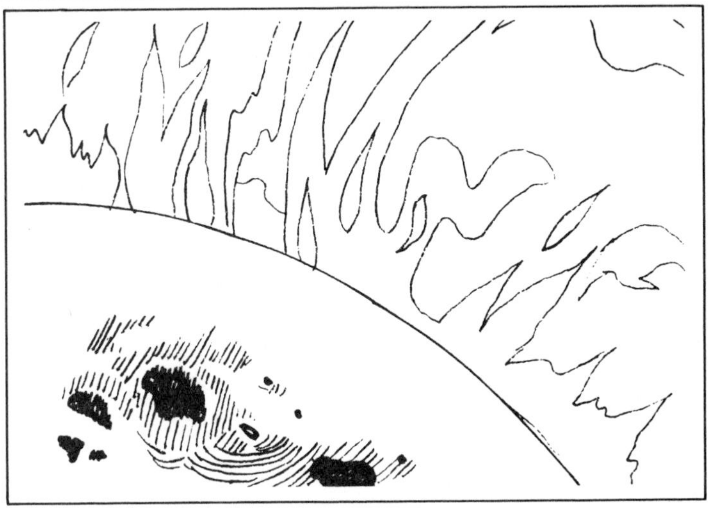

Main Idea

1. This story tells about

   _____ the Aurora Borealis.

   _____ ozones.

   _____ sunspots.

Sequencing

2. Number the events below in the order that they happened.

   _____ Galileo invented the telescope.

   _____ Astronomers studied the sunspots.

   _____ They decided that sunspots were huge storms on the sun.

   _____ Galileo saw large black spots on the sun.

Reading for Details

3. Use the clues to answer these questions.

   What are sunspots? (paragraph 2) _____

   _____

   Where are sunspots located? (paragraph 2) _____

   _____

   Why do sunspots look black to us? (paragraph 2) _____

   _____

   What changes are caused by sunspots? (paragraph 3) _____

   _____

   Who studies sunspots? (paragraph 2) _____

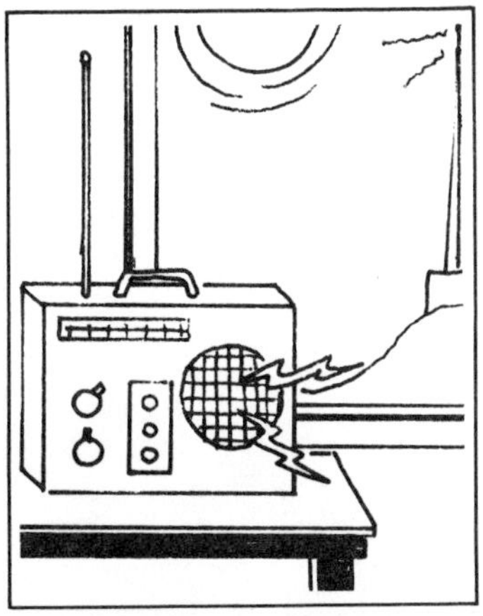

Reading for Understanding

4. Circle Yes or No.

Sunspots affect the earth.	Yes	No
The Aurora Borealis is dreary when there are many sunspots.	Yes	No
The ozone layer becomes thinner when there are many sunspots.	Yes	No
Sunspots interfere with radio signals and make it hard to hear.	Yes	No

The Sun Followers

Plants don't have legs to run or arms to throw a baseball. But that doesn't mean that plants can't move at all. If you watch closely, you will see that most plants bend their stems and flowers toward the sunlight every day. Perhaps you have seen your mother turn her houseplants around because the whole plant is leaning toward the window. How are plants able to move when they don't have bodies like animals do?

Plant cells make chemicals called auxins to help them move. To find out how these chemicals work, think of a plant outside in a garden. Because the sun rises in the east, in the morning the east side of the plant stem is in the light. But the west side of the stem is in the shade. So the cells in the shaded side of the stem begin to make auxins. The auxins make that side of the stem grow fast, while the side of the stem toward the sun grows much slower. When the shaded side grows faster, it makes the whole stem bend toward the sunlight. And any leaves or flowers on the stem face the sun too. When the sun moves to the west in the afternoon, the west side of the stem, which was in the shade, is now in the light. Now the cells in the east side of the plant begin to make auxins, and the stem bends toward the light again.

There is a reason why the plant produces chemicals that make stems follow the sun. Leaves use sunlight to make food for the plant, so it is important for them to get as much light as they can. By following the sun, the leaves can make food all day. So by making the stems bend, auxins really help leaves to always face their energy supply, the sun.

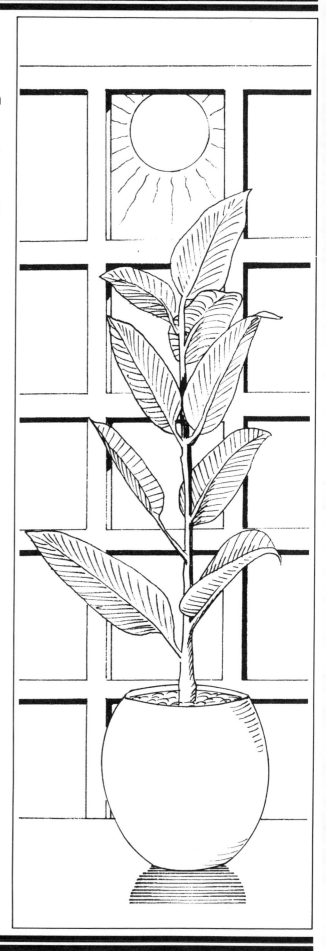

Name _____

The Sun Followers

Main Idea

1. This story explains

_____ how plants move.

_____ how the sun comes up in the east.

_____ how plants make food with sunshine.

Sequencing

2. Number the events below in the order that they happen.

_____ The cells in the shaded west side of the stem begin to make auxins.

_____ The plant bends to face the sun.

_____ In the morning, the east side of the plant stem is in the light.

_____ The west side of the stem grows fast.

Reading for Details

3. Use the clues to answer these questions.

Why do plants move? (paragraph 1 & 3) _____

_____

What chemical helps plants move? (paragraph 2) _____

Where are auxins located? (paragraph 2) _____

When are auxins produced by the plant? (paragraph 2) _____

_____

How do leaves use sunlight? (paragraph 3) _____

_____

Reading for Understanding

4. Choose the correct topic for each paragraph.

Paragraph 2   Paragraph 3

_____ plant stems   _____ why plants always face the sun

_____ auxins   _____ why plants make food

_____ sunlight   _____ why plants produce auxins

The Earth's Safety Blanket

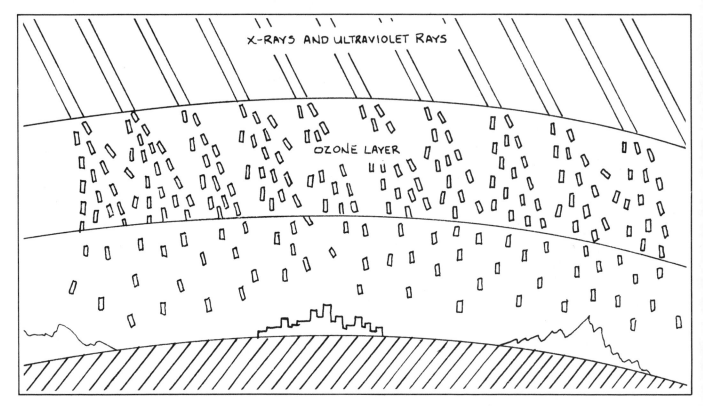

A few years ago, whenever people used hair spray or insect spray or spray paint, they were destroying an important part of our world. Although no one knew it, the gases in spray cans were harming the ozone layer.

No one has ever seen the ozone layer because it isn't on the earth. It is part of the atmosphere, a thick blanket of air that covers the world. The atmosphere is made up of many gases, especially nitrogen and oxygen. Close to the earth, the atmosphere is thick and heavy, but as it gets farther away from the earth, the atmosphere gets thin. There, the energy from the sun changes the way the gases behave. For instance, oxygen atoms usually travel in the air connected together in pairs. But high in the atmosphere, the sun's energy causes three oxygen atoms to connect together instead of two. These groups of three oxygen atoms are called ozone. And the place high in the air where regular oxygen changes to ozone is called the ozone layer.

The ozone layer is very important to life on earth even though it is far away. It soaks up dangerous rays from the sun that harm plants and animals. Even more important, the ozone layer helps keep the earth cool. Without it, the earth might become so hot that the icecaps would melt and flood much of the world. That is why scientists were worried when they found out that gases from spray cans were destroying the ozone layer. Now spray cans contain safe gases. So even though some of the ozone layer has been destroyed, it is no longer being harmed by people's spray cans.

The Earth's Safety Blanket

Main Idea

1. This story explains

_____ the use of spray cans.

_____ the ozone layer of the atmosphere.

_____ the dangerous rays of the sun.

Sequencing

2. Number the events below in the order that they happened.

_____ Spray cans were changed to contain safe gases.

_____ Scientists became worried about the ozone layer.

_____ People using spray cans were destroying the ozone layer.

_____ The ozone layer was no longer being harmed by spray cans.

Reading for Details

3. Use the clues to answer these questions.

What is the atmosphere made of? (paragraph 2) _____

_____

Where is the atmosphere thick and heavy? (paragraph 2) _____

_____

Where is it thinner? (paragraph 2) _____

Why is the ozone layer important to the earth? (paragraph 3) _____

_____

How was the ozone layer being harmed? (paragraph 1) _____

OXYGEN ATOMS IN THE OZONE LAYER

OXYGEN ATOMS IN THE AIR WE BREATHE

Reading for Understanding

4. Place the correct letter in the blank.

_____ ozone layer

_____ atmosphere

_____ ozone

_____ spray cans

a. thick blanket of air that covers the earth

b. groups of three oxygen atoms

c. place high in the atmosphere where regular oxygen changes to ozone

d. used to contain harmful gases

The Ups and Downs of the Barometer

Every day on the radio or television, you can hear the weather forecaster say, "The barometer is thirty inches and falling," or "The barometer is twenty-nine inches and rising." Barometers must have something to do with the weather. But what really rises and falls? And what do the inches measure?

A barometer measures air pressure. The air around us has weight, and this weight is called air pressure. But the air doesn't always have the same weight. Sometimes the air is light, and we say the air pressure is low. When the air is heavy, we say the air pressure is high. Barometers tell just how high or low the air pressure is.

A barometer is made of a long tube with a heavy silver liquid called mercury. The tube is closed at the top, and the bottom of the tube stands in a dish of mercury. When the air presses on the mercury, it pushes some of the mercury into the tube. The higher the air pressure is, the more mercury it pushes up into the tube. When the air pressure becomes lower, the air doesn't press as hard on the dish of mercury. So some of it comes out of the tube and back into the dish. The height of the mercury in the tube is measured in inches.

Warm, moist air is usually light, and has low pressure. So a falling barometer can forecast a warm, rainy day. On the other hand, cool, dry air is heavy and has high pressure. When the barometer rises, look for a dry, sunny day. As you can see, the barometer's ups and downs are the weather forecaster's best friend.

Name _____

The Ups and Downs of the Barometer

Main Idea
1. Choose another title for this story.

_____ The Weather Forecaster's Best Friend

_____ Light Air and Heavy Air

_____ Weather Reports

Sequencing
2. Number the events below in the order that they happen.

_____ Some of the mercury comes out of the tube and goes back into the dish.

_____ The air pressure gets lower.

_____ Some of the mercury pushes into the tube.

_____ Air presses on the mercury at the bottom of the tube.

Reading for Details
3. Use the clues to answer these questions.

Who reports the barometer readings on radio and television? (paragraph 1) _____

_____

Why is the barometer an important tool? (paragraph 4) _____

_____

What makes the mercury rise and fall in the barometer? (paragraph 3) _____

_____

When is the air pressure high? (paragraph 2) _____

_____

What happens to the mercury in the barometer when the air pressure is high?

(paragraph 3) _____

Reading for Understanding
4. Place the correct letter in the blank.

_____ barometer   a. forecasts a warm, rainy day

_____ mercury   b. a heavy, silver liquid

_____ falling barometer   c. forecasts a dry, sunny day

_____ rising barometer   d. means air is light

_____ low air pressure   e. instrument which measures air pressure by inches

_____ high air pressure   f. means air is heavy

Help for Rare Animals

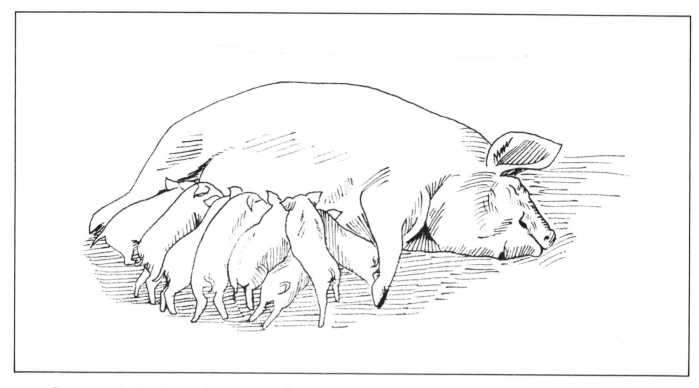

On a certain farm in the English countryside, cattle and sheep graze in the fields. Pigs lie in the mud, and chickens scratch in the barnyard. But the animals on this farm are not ordinary animals. They are the last of their kind, and they are fighting to survive.

People who work at this special farm, called the Rare Breed Animal Trust, are doing their best to help these animals. When any kind of animal becomes almost extinct, the few animals left are often not very healthy. They have few babies, and those often die. To help the animals become healthier, the workers at the Survival Trust take care of the babies and raise them carefully. Then they cross-breed, or mix, the rare animals with other animals that look like them. The babies from this cross-breeding are healthier and stronger than their parents. After a few years, the animals are no longer in danger of dying out.

For instance, the four-horned Jacob's sheep was once seen often in Arabia. But over the years, fewer and fewer of them survived, and the Jacob's sheep became an endangered species. Then a few last sheep were brought to the Survival Trust. The people there bred them with some similar sheep, and now many more Jacob's sheep play in the farm's fields. Soon they can be taken back to live in Arabia.

The Survival Trust can even make copies of extinct animals. By cross-breeding several kinds of pigs, they have bred a pig like one that lived a thousand years ago. So if you ever see a dinosaur or a mammoth playing in the country, they may have come from the Survival Trust Farm.

Help for Rare Animals

Main Idea
1. Choose another title for this story.

_____ The Story of Cross-Breeding

_____ The Jacob's Sheep

_____ The Rare Breed Animal Trust

Sequencing
2. Number the events below in the order that they happened.

_____ The sheep became an endangered species and were taken to the Survival Trust Farm.

_____ The sheep were bred with some similar sheep.

_____ The Jacob's sheep was common in Arabia.

_____ Jacob's sheep will be taken back to live in Arabia.

Reading for Details
3. Use the clues to answer these questions.

Where is the Survival Trust Farm? (paragraph 1) _____

_____

What kinds of animals live on the farm? (paragraph 1 & 2) _____

_____

When are animals brought to the farm? (paragraph 2) _____

_____

Who helps the rare animals? (paragraph 2) _____

_____

Why do the farm workers take care of the baby animals and raise them

carefully? (paragraph 2) _____

Reading for Understanding
4. Choose the topic of Paragraph 4.

_____ making copies of extinct animals

_____ living thousands of years ago

_____ farming today

North America in the Ice Age

Suppose you were able to go back in time. You arrive in Canada and the northern United States 20,000 years ago, expecting to see forests and lakes. But instead, huge ice sheets, called glaciers, cover the earth for thousands of miles. You have entered the Ice Age.

Long ago, as the earth got colder, glaciers formed near the North Pole and began slowly moving south. Because the earth was cold, the glaciers didn't melt. They grew until they covered all of North America as far south as Ohio. As they moved, they scraped the soil and rock from the earth and carried them along. The slowly moving ice, rock, and soil were so heavy that they ground great holes in the earth and made wide valleys. For 10,000 years the glaciers kept moving south.

When the earth warmed up again, the glaciers began to melt. As they did, they left behind a land that looked very different than it had looked before. Huge piles of rock, called moraines, stood where the melting glacier had dropped them. Chunks of ice broke off the glacier and were buried. When they melted, they formed deep kettle lakes. But the biggest change of all happened at what is now the border between the United States and Canada. Five huge lakes appeared where no lakes had been before. The glacier had scraped out the Great Lakes, then filled them with water as it melted. The Ice Age was over, but it had left its mark on the land.

Today in the western U.S. and Canada, small glaciers move slowly down the mountain sides. They are nothing like the huge glaciers of the Ice Age. But they remind us of the giant part glaciers played in shaping North America.

North America in the Ice Age

Main Idea

1. Choose another title for this story.

_____ Ice, Rock, and Soil

_____ Formation of the Great Lakes

_____ A Continent Shaped by Glaciers

Sequencing

2. Number the events below in the order that they happened.

_____ Huge glaciers began slowly moving south.

_____ They scraped the soil and rock from the earth.

_____ The glaciers began to melt.

_____ The earth warmed up.

_____ The Great Lakes were formed.

Reading for Details

3. Use the clues to answer these questions.

When was the Ice Age? (paragraph 1) _____

What caused the Ice Age? (paragraph 2) _____

_____

Why were great holes and wide valleys made by the glaciers? (paragraph 2) _____

_____

Where did the biggest change in the earth's surface occur? (paragraph 3) _____

_____

Why was the Ice Age important? (paragraph 3) _____

_____

THE GREAT LAKES TODAY

Reading for Understanding

4. Place the correct letter in the blank.

_____ glaciers   a. buried chunks of ice that melted

_____ moraines   b. 20,000 years ago

_____ Ice Age   c. huge piles of rock left by glaciers

_____ kettle lakes   d. huge ice sheets

_____ Great Lakes   e. huge lakes shaped and filled by melting glaciers

Cleaning Up— How Soap Works

How many times have you come in from outdoors with dirty hands and dirty clothes? Without even thinking, you wash your hands with soap and water and put your clothes in the washing machine. Magically, everything is clean again. What is the magic of soap? How does it take away dirt that water by itself won't remove?

When soap is added to water, it works in two ways to get rid of dirt and grease. Water by itself does not mix well with dirt. It floats on top or around it, but water by itself won't wash most dirt away. But when it mixes with water, soap makes the water "wetter." Although it sounds strange, wetter water is able to flow around and under dirt particles and float them away.

Second, soap makes the dirt stick to water because soap has a special shape. Each particle of soap is a long thin rod with a head end and a tail end. When soap meets water, the head end of the soap particle attaches itself to a water molecule. Then the tail end of the soap buries itself in a dirt or grease particle. Now the dirt particle and the water molecule are joined together. Many soap particles may stick to one dirt particle, so the dirt becomes surrounded by soap and water. The dirt floats away in the water, and your hands or clothes are clean.

Soap works well in most water. When it doesn't, detergents take over. They do the same job as soap, but they can work in water that makes soap lose its cleaning power. Soap and detergent are two of the most important products in the world. If there was no soap, how could you ever wash up before dinner?

74

Name _____

Cleaning Up—
How Soap Works

Main Idea

1. Choose another title for this story.

_____ Dirt and Grease

_____ Washing Your Hands

_____ The Magic of Soap

Sequencing

2. Number the events below in the order that they happen.

_____ Soap meets water.

_____ The dirt becomes surrounded by soap and water.

_____ The dirt floats away in the water.

_____ The head end of the soap particle attaches itself to a water molecule.

_____ The tail end of the soap buries itself into a dirt or grease particle.

Reading for Details.

3. Use the clues to answer these questions.

What works together to wash away dirt? (paragraph 2) _____

_____

Why does water need help to wash away dirt? (paragraph 2) _____

_____

When do detergents take over? (paragraph 4) _____

_____

Where does the dirt go? (paragraph 3) _____

_____

Why are soap and detergent such important products? (paragraph 4) _____

_____

Reading for Understanding

4. Circle Yes or No.

I make water "wetter."	Yes	No
I have a special shape that makes dirt stick to water.	Yes	No
My head end attaches to a dirt molecule.	Yes	No
My tail end buries itself in a water molecule.	Yes	No
My partner, detergent, helps when I just can't do the job.	Yes	No

Parasites—Life from Life

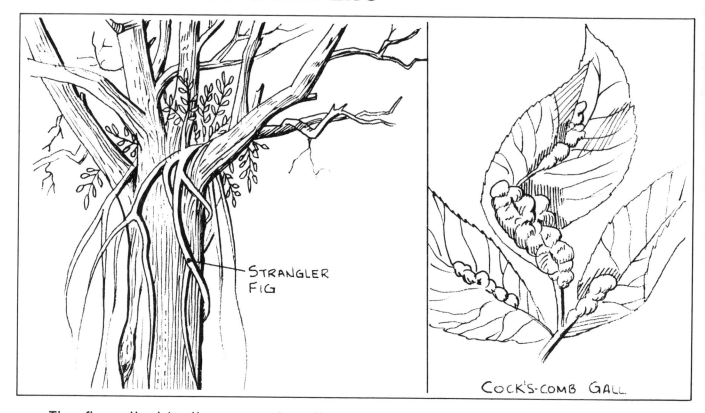

STRANGLER FIG

COCK'S-COMB GALL

The fleas that bother your dog, the bacteria that make you sick, and the mistletoe that you see every Christmas have something in common. They cannot survive by themselves. They are all parasites, and if they could not feed on some other living plant or animal, they would die.

A parasite lives on or inside another plant or animal, which is called the host. Animals like dogs or cats are hosts for fleas and ticks, while people are hosts for the bacteria that cause disease. The parasite gets its food by actually eating its host while it is alive. For example, fleas, ticks, and leeches puncture the skin of animals and suck their blood. Bacteria get inside the cells of plants and animals and use the cells for food. Worms, such as tapeworms and roundworms, get inside the digestive systems of animals when the animals swallow the worm's eggs. When the eggs hatch, the worms attach themselves to the host's intestines and use the food the host eats. Plant parasites push their roots deep into the host plant and steal the sugar the host makes for itself. Mistletoe is a plant parasite that grows on the branches of oak trees. It can make its own food, but its roots take water and minerals from the oak instead of taking them from the soil.

All parasites make their hosts weaker. A few fleas will not harm your dog very much, but a tapeworm can take so much food from its human host that the person becomes sick. People have been trying for thousands of years to kill these pests. But in spite of all science can do, these creatures continue to take their life from others.

Parasites— Life from Life

FLEA

TRICHINA WORM
LODGED IN
MUSCLE FIBER

Main Idea

1. This story explains

_____ how mistletoe takes water from oak trees.

_____ how parasites take their food from others.

_____ how dogs and cats get fleas.

Sequencing

2. Number the events below in the order that they happen.

_____ An animal swallows tapeworm eggs.

_____ The worms attach themselves to the host's intestines.

_____ The worm uses the food that the animal eats.

_____ The eggs hatch.

_____ The host becomes weak.

Reading for Details

3. Use the clues to answer these questions.

How does a parasite get its food? (paragraph 2) _____

_____

Who is harmed by parasites? (paragraph 2) _____

What is a host? (paragraph 2) _____

_____

What do plant parasites take from their hosts? (paragraph 2) _____

_____

How is mistletoe different from other plant parasites? (paragraph 2) _____

_____

SHEEP
TICK

Reading for Understanding

4. Choose the topic for each paragraph.

Paragraph 2	Paragraph 3
_____ how parasites get food	_____ what you should know about your dog
_____ how tapeworms grow	_____ what parasites do to hosts
_____ how mistletoe lives	_____ how mistletoe lives

The Ghost Fish

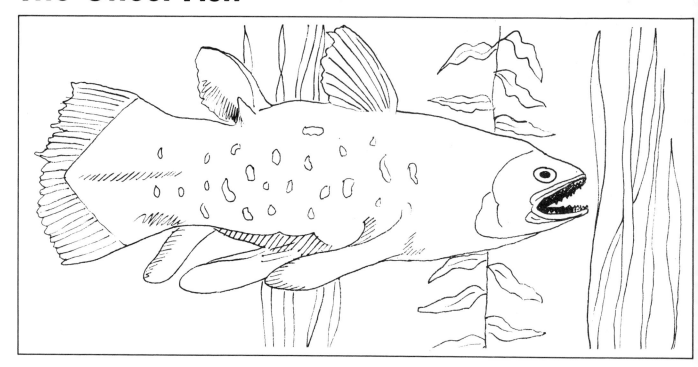

One bright day, a few years ago, some fishermen in Africa pulled their nets out of the Atlantic Ocean to see what they had caught. The ordinary fish they caught every day flopped around in the net. But then the men looked closer and their eyes grew wide. In the bottom of the net was the strangest fish they had ever seen.

The men brought the fish to some scientists, who thought they were seeing a ghost. The fish, called a coelecanth, was supposed to have disappeared millions of years ago. The coelecanth was one of the earliest fishes. It was shaped much like fish today, but it had fleshy fins that looked like very short legs. Its scales were not thin and shiny like the scales of fish we know. Instead, the coelecanth was covered with big bony plates that looked almost like armor. Its big eyes and huge mouth helped it find enough food in the dark deep waters where it lived.

Then, three hundred million years ago, faster and smarter fish began to rule the oceans, and the coelecanths died away. At least scientists thought they had all died. But here was a living fossil, an animal no human had ever seen before! No one knows how the coelecanth survived. No one knows, either, why the coelecanth suddenly appeared after hiding for so long. But scientists think that the coelecanth might have started to run out of food. When it came up to the shallow water to look for its dinner, it was caught in the fishermen's net. Since then, more coelecanths have been seen, so scientists know the living fossil is still with us today.

Coelecanth is pronounced sēl'a canth.

Name _____

The Ghost Fish

Main Idea

1. This story tells about

_____ a fish that scientists thought was extinct.

_____ fishermen in Africa.

_____ the Atlantic Ocean.

Sequencing

2. Number the events below in the order that they happened.

_____ The scientists thought they were seeing a ghost.

_____ Fishermen in Africa caught a fish.

_____ Scientists determined the fish to be a coelecanth.

_____ They took the fish to some scientists.

_____ More coelecanths were seen by other people.

Reading for Details

3. Use the clues to answer these questions.

What was found in the bottom of the fishing net? (paragraph 1) _____

_____

Why did the fishermen think the fish was strange? (paragraph 2) _____

_____

Where did the coelecanth live? (paragraph 2) _____

When did scientists think the coelecanth had died away? (paragraph 3) _____

_____

Why did the coelecanth suddenly appear? (paragraph 3) _____

_____

Reading for Understanding

4. Circle Yes or No.

I am one of the earliest fishes.	Yes	No
My fins look like very short legs.	Yes	No
I am covered with shiny, bony scales.	Yes	No
I have tiny eyes.	Yes	No
I have a huge mouth.	Yes	No
I live in deep, dark waters.	Yes	No
I am a living fossil.	Yes	No
I am extinct.	Yes	No

When the Body Tries Too Hard

On the finest summer or fall days, some people's eyes water and swell. Their heads stuff up, and they sneeze as though they had terrible colds. Other people get a red, itchy rash when they eat certain foods. These people all have allergies, and their misery is caused by their bodies trying too hard to keep them healthy.

In a way, the body has its own police force, called the immune system. When something that causes disease – bacteria, for example – gets into the body, the immune system goes to work. Chemicals called antibodies, trap the bacteria in the blood. Then white blood cells come along and eat the bacteria. Special cells make histimine, which causes watery eyes and a runny nose. Although the sneezing and stuffiness are no fun, they help get rid of even more bacteria and protect the body.

But some people's immune systems try too hard to protect them. They begin to fight harmless things like dirt, pollen, or even food. When this happens, we say the person has an allergy. The histimine causes skin rash, swelling, and a stuffy head. Sometimes, histimine may cause a person to be sick enough to go to a hospital.

Nobody knows why some people's bodies fight harmless things. But scientists do know that allergies usually run in families. Sometimes doctors try to cure allergies by giving the patient a very small amount of whatever causes the allergy every week for a year or two. This way, the body may get used to the substance and not fight against it. So even though allergies can cause misery and suffering, people should remember that the body is only trying to help.

When the Body Tries Too Hard

Main Idea

1. This story tells about

_____ antihistamines.

_____ allergies.

_____ stuffy noses.

Sequencing

2. Number the events below in the order that they happen.

_____ The person gets watery eyes and a runny nose.

_____ Antibodies trap the bacteria in the blood.

_____ Bacteria get into a person's system.

_____ White blood cells eat the bacteria.

_____ Special cells make histamine.

Reading for Details

3. Use the clues to answer these questions.

What does the immune system do? (paragraph 2) _____

_____

Why do some people get allergies? (paragraph 1) _____

_____

Where are allergy victims likely to go if they get sick enough? (paragraph 3) _____

_____

Why does histamine make us uncomfortable? (paragraph 2) _____

_____

Reading for Understanding

4. Place the correct letter in the blank.

_____ immune system   a. eat bacteria

_____ antibodies   b. body's own police force

_____ white blood cells   c. causes watery eyes and a runny nose

_____ histamine   d. trap bacteria in the blood

_____ bacteria   e. something that causes disease

A New Old Sport

Many people in the North wait eagerly for the first snows of winter to come. Then they grab their skis and poles and head outside for a day of skiing fun. Because there are so many special ski hills and ski trails, you may think skiing is a new sport. But skiing is a very old way to travel, and it did not start as a sport.

Skiing started in Norway thousands of years ago. People have found Stone Age carvings and drawings of people on skis in Norway and Finland. The Laplanders, who live in northern Finland, even had a goddess of skiing. Old statues show her wearing skis with curved toes.

Skis were always very important to the people of Norway, Sweden, and Finland. In the long, snowy winter, people had to ski to get from place to place. Even today, the Laplanders follow their reindeer herds on skis. And in northern Europe, Canada, and the United States, some people still do much of their winter traveling on skis.

Today there are two main kinds of skiing. The oldest, and most useful, is cross-country skiing. Cross-country skiers use skis to walk from place to place. They can go almost anywhere—uphill, downhill, or on flat ground. Now there are special cross-country ski trails, but old roads or hiking trails work as well.

Downhill skiing needs a mountain or a steep hill. Skiers ride ski lifts to the top of the hill. Then they push off on their skies and have an exciting trip to the bottom, where they take the lift back to the top again.

Both kinds of skiing are great fun. It is lucky that long ago someone had to travel on snow and invented skis to do it.

Name _____

A New Old Sport

Main Idea
1. Choose another title for this story.

_____ The Goddess of Skiing

_____ The People of Norway

_____ Skiing–Transportation and Sport

Sequencing
2. Number the events below in the order that they happened.

_____ Skiing started in Norway thousands of years ago.

_____ Skiing became a sport for people in many countries.

_____ The Laplanders began to follow their reindeer herds on skis.

_____ Skiing spread from Norway to Sweden and Finland.

Reading for Details
3. Use the clues to answer these questions.

Who are the Laplanders? (paragraph 2) _____

_____

How do the Laplanders use skis? (paragraph 3) _____

_____

Where did skiing start? (paragraph 2) _____

When did people begin skiing? (paragraph 2) _____

What information do we have that tells us when people began skiing? (paragraph 2)

_____

Why do people like to ski? (paragraph 6) _____

_____

Reading for Understanding
4. Write the phrase in the correct column.

oldest and most useful, needs a mountain or hill,
walk from place to place, ride ski lifts to the top,
go almost anywhere, exciting trip to the bottom

Cross-country Skiing	Downhill Skiing
_____	_____
_____	_____
_____	_____

Buried Treasure

Have you ever read stories about sunken treasure buried at the bottom of the ocean? Maybe you have thought how exciting it would be to look for buried gold. But, you may say, people only find treasure in story books.

A man in Florida would not agree with you. He has found not one, but eight sunken ships loaded with gold and silver. It all started one day when the man was walking along the beach. He saw something shiny in the sand and stopped to pick it up. To his surprise, it was a "piece of eight," an old Spanish coin of pure gold.

Many other people would have just taken the coin and gone away. But this man became curious. He looked at old maps and read history books until he found out where the coin came from. In the year 1715, ten Spanish ships had been carrying gold, silver, and jewels from South America to Spain. But they sank during a storm. "Perhaps," thought the man, "the ships and their treasure are still at the bottom of the ocean."

He decided to find them. First he took an airplane and flew out over the ocean. Near the beach, he spotted a big dark shape under the water. Marking the spot on a map, he and some friends dove down near the shape. There, at the bottom of the sea, they found one of the ships they had been looking for. It was broken and rotting, but in the mud and sand were silver coins. When the men cleaned away layers of mud from the ocean floor, they found more than a thousand gold pieces. Later they found seven more ships, each holding gold and silver from South America. They had truly discovered buried treasure!

Buried Treasure

Main Idea
1. This story tells about

_____ a man who was a treasure hunter.

_____ a big dark spot under the water.

_____ ten Spanish ships that sank in 1715.

Sequencing
2. Number the events below in the order that they happened.

_____ He read about ten ships that had sunk.

_____ A man in Florida found a gold coin on the beach.

_____ He flew an airplane over the ocean.

_____ He and his friends found one of the ships near the beach.

Reading for Details
3. Use the clues to answer these questions.

Who would not agree that people only find treasure in story books? (paragraph 2) _____

_____

What did he find as he was walking along the beach? (paragraph 2) _____

_____

Where did he look to find out where the coin came from? (paragraph 3) _____

_____

Why did the man want to know about the gold coin? (paragraph 3) _____

_____

When did the ten Spanish ships sink? (paragraph 3) _____

Reading for Understanding
4. Choose the topic for paragraph 2.

_____ a Florida beach

_____ a man who believes in buried treasure

_____ a gold coin

A Gift from the Trees

Nothing tastes quite so good on breakfast pancakes or waffles as maple syrup. The Indians in eastern Canada made maple syrup a long time ago. The Indians in the northern part of the United States made it too. Then the settlers came, and they learned how to make this treat. Making maple syrup takes a long time, so people who make syrup begin work before the winter snow melts.

Maple syrup comes from the sap of maple trees. Just before spring comes, the trees send sugar and water up from their roots to their branches. This sugar and water mixture is the sap. All maple trees will give sap, but only trees with big trunks can give sap for syrup without being hurt. People who make syrup look for sugar maples and black maples, because they have the best sap for syrup.

When they find the right tree, the syrup makers hammer a tube called a "spout" into the tree trunk. Then they hang a bucket under the spout. The sap drips out through the spout and falls into the bucket. When the bucket is full, the syrup makers pour the sap into a big pot. Then the cooking begins. The pot of sap boils all day on a stove, and once in a while, people stir the boiling sap. The smell of maple syrup floats outside, making everyone hungry. Boiling makes the water in the sap evaporate, and the sap gets thick. When it gets thick enough, the sap becomes maple syrup.

It takes a great deal of sap to make syrup. One maple tree gives fifteen to twenty gallons of sap. But all this sap only makes two quarts of syrup. People who make syrup must own many trees and work hard. But the taste of maple syrup in the morning makes all the work worthwhile.

A Gift from the Trees

Main Idea

1. This story explains

_____ what kinds of trees have the best sap for syrup.

_____ how maple syrup is made.

_____ where maple syrup is sold.

Sequencing

2. Number the events below in the order that they happen.

_____ The syrup makers cook the sap all day.

_____ The sap gets thick and becomes maple syrup.

_____ Syrup makers hammer a spout into the tree trunk.

_____ The sap drops through the spout into a bucket.

Reading for Details

3. Use the clues to answer these questions.

Who made maple syrup a long time ago? (paragraph 1) _____

_____

What kinds of trees have the best sap for syrup? (paragraph 2) _____

_____

Where do the syrup makers hang the bucket? (paragraph 3) _____

_____

When do the syrup makers pour the sap into a big pot? (paragraph 3) _____

_____

Why do the syrup makers boil the sap? (paragraph 3) _____

_____

Reading for Understanding

4. Check the correct answer(s).

Sugar maples and black maples are used for making maple syrup because

_____ they are big enough.

_____ they are abundant.

_____ they have a lot of sap.

_____ they have the best sap.

The Roman Highway

When people drive long distances today, they usually drive on brand new superhighways. Most large highways in the United States and Canada are so new that people think a forty or fifty-year-old highway is old. But near the city of Rome, in Italy, there is a much older highway, called the Appian Way. Though the Appian Way is more than 2,000 years old, it is still used for travel.

The Romans built this great road when they had just started to rule all of Italy. They wanted a way to move their armies and to trade with the people they had conquered. For trade, there must be good roads for merchants to travel on. So in 312 B.C., Appius Claudius, who was the Roman emperor, ordered a highway to be built. It was to stretch 360 miles, or 580 kilometers, from Rome to the southern end of Italy.

Workers started building the highway right away. And Appius Claudius kept checking the work every day. Although he was blind, Appius felt the roadway with his feet to make sure it was smooth enough. Appius died before the highway was finished, but the work kept on. Sixteen years after it was started, the Appian Way, named after Appius Claudius, was ready for travelers.

Road builders today are amazed at how well the Appian Way was built. In some places, the sand, gravel, and rock that make up the road are five feet, or 1.5 meters, thick. Modern roads are usually only half that thick, even though they must carry heavier loads. But modern roads are not as sturdy as Roman roads. The Romans built their roads to last, for today, after 2,000 years, people and cars still travel the Appian Way.

Appius Claudius is pronounced ap'i us clạ'di us.

Name _____

The Roman Highway

Main Idea
1. Choose another title for this story.

_____ Appius Claudius

_____ American Roads vs. Roman Roads

_____ Building an Old Highway

Sequencing
2. Number the events below in the order that they happened.

_____ Appius Claudius checked the work every day.

_____ Appius Claudius died before the highway was finished.

_____ Workers started building the highway.

_____ Emperor Appius Claudius ordered a highway to be built.

Reading for Details
3. Use the clues to answer these questions.

Who built the Appian Way? (paragraph 2) _____

What materials were used to build the Appian Way? (paragraph 4) _____

_____

When did Appius Claudius order the highway to be built? (paragraph 2) _____

_____

Where is the highway located? (paragraph 2) _____

_____

Why did Appius Claudius want the highway built? (paragraph 2) _____

_____

Reading for Understanding
4. Circle the correct answer.

I (could, could not) see.

I felt the roadway with my (hands, feet) every day to make sure it was smooth.

The highway (was, was not) named after me.

In some places, the road is (1.5 m, 7.5 m) thick.

The First Painters

All groups of people in the world paint pictures, and people have been painting pictures for a very long time. The Egyptians used watercolors to paint pictures of their kings 3000 years ago. But people have been painting pictures even longer than that.

The very first painters must have been cave people. In 1875, some people who were exploring caves in Spain noticed drawings on the walls of the caves. These drawings were of wild animals that had not lived in Spain for thousands of years. Scientists who saw the drawings said cave people who lived 30,000 years ago had made the animal pictures! They are the oldest drawings we know of today.

These cave artists used bright yellow, orange, and brown paints to make the animal pictures. We think they made paints by grinding colored rock on soil into a powder. Then they mixed the powder with animal fat until the powder became a paste. For paint brushes, the people may have used animal hairs tied to sticks, or perhaps stems of plants. They may even have had crayons. If the powder-fat paste was made very thick and then left to dry, it would form sticks. The cave artists could then have used the sticks as we use chalk or crayons.

No one knows why cave people began painting pictures. They may have believed that drawing pictures of the animals they hunted would bring them good luck. Or perhaps they painted just for fun, as people do today. What better way to brighten up the dull walls of their cave homes?

The First Painters

Main Idea
1. Choose another title for this story.

_____ Exploring Caves

_____ How to Make Paints

_____ Cave Artists

Sequencing
2. Number the events below in the order that they happened.

_____ They noticed drawings on the wall.

_____ People were exploring caves in Spain.

_____ The scientists determined that the cave people drew them 30,000 years ago.

_____ Scientists then saw the drawings.

Reading for Details
3. Use the clues to answer these questions.

Who used watercolors to paint pictures 3,000 years ago? (paragraph 1) _____

_____

What did some cave explorers find in 1875? (paragraph 2) _____

_____

Where were the caves located in which the pictures were found? (paragraph 2) _____

_____

When did scientists say the drawings were made? (paragraph 2) _____

_____

Why did cave people paint pictures? (paragraph 4) _____

_____

Reading for Understanding
4. Check the correct answer(s).

The cave artists may have painted because

_____ they believed that drawing pictures of the animals they hunted would bring them good luck.

_____ they thought it was fun.

_____ they wanted to decorate their cave walls.

A Real Family Tree

Perhaps your family has a "family tree." It may be a chart on the wall or in a family book that tells the names of all your relatives as far back as anyone can remember. Some Indian tribes of western Canada and the western United States have family trees too. But these family trees are made from real trees, and they are called "totem poles."

Indian people who use totem poles form themselves into groups called clans. All the people in a clan believe they come from the same ancestor. The ancestor, they say, started the clan, and each clan tells old stories about its ancestor. But this ancestor is not always a person. It may be an animal or a plant. When this happens, the animal or plant is called the "totem" of the clan. The clan pays special honor to its totem. If a clan's totem is the fox, the clan will be named the "fox clan." None of the clan members must ever harm a fox, for the fox protects the people of its clan.

Often the clan will make a totem pole to show that it is proud of its ancestor. On the top of a pole, the people carve a picture of their totem animal. Under the totem animal, they carve other animals or people who are important in the stories of the clan. So on one long pole, the clan shows its whole history. Totem poles may be fifty feet, or 15 meters, tall, and they are usually painted bright colors. The totem pole is set up in the middle of the clan's village so that even from far away, people can see the clan's history.

Totem poles are colorful and pretty. But they are important too. They help a clan remember its history and teach that history to its children.

92

Name _____

A Real Family Tree

Main Idea

1. Choose another title for this story.

_____ How to Make a Totem Pole

_____ History in a Totem Pole

_____ Indian Ancestors

Sequencing

2. Number the events below in the order that they happen.

_____ Other animals or people important in the clan's stories are carved under the totem.

_____ A picture of the clan's totem is carved on the top of the pole.

_____ Indians form themselves into groups called clans.

_____ The totem pole is set up in the middle of the village where it can be seen from far away.

Reading for Details

3. Use the clues to answer these questions.

What is a family tree? (paragraph 1) _____

_____

What are family trees called that are made from real trees? (paragraph 1) _____

_____

Where do the Indian tribes live who make totem poles?(paragraph 1) _____

_____

What is the "totem" of the clan? (paragraph 2) _____

_____

Why are totem poles important? (paragraph 4) _____

_____

Reading for Understanding

4. Choose the topic for paragraph 3.

_____ how the clan shows its history

_____ where a clan sets up its totem pole

_____ how the clan makes its totem pole

The Fastest Mail in the West

Today when you drop a letter to a friend into a mailbox, you know that your letter will arrive at your friend's house in a few days. Trucks and airplanes carry mail quickly from place to place. But in the United States in the 1850's, there were no trucks or airplanes. If you wanted to send a letter to a friend across the country, you mailed the letter and let the stagecoach carry it with the rest of the mail. But the stagecoach was slow. The letter would take weeks or even months to get to your friend. What if the letter had important news? There was no way to get important mail from place to place quickly.

Then in 1860, the United States government started the Pony Express, the fastest mail service in the country. The route ran from St. Joseph, Missouri, to California, across high mountains and through hot, dry deserts. With the mail in a saddlebag, a young rider would gallop off alone from St. Joseph on a fast horse. Fifteen miles farther on, he would come to a little station. There a fresh horse would be waiting, and the rider would jump on the new horse and keep riding. Each Pony Express rider would ride a hundred miles, changing horses every fifteen miles. Then another rider would take over. Stopping only to change horses, the Pony Express team could carry the mail over 1,000 miles in only ten days.

The Pony Express was one of the most famous services in United States history. But it lasted for only one year. In 1861, the telegraph, which could send messages in minutes, connected the East and the West. And the Pony Express disappeared forever.

Name _____

The Fastest Mail in the West

Main Idea
1. Choose another title for this story.

_____ The Pony Express

_____ The Telegraph

_____ The U.S. Government in 1860

Sequencing
2. Number the events below in the order that they happened.

_____ Fifteen miles later he would come to a little station.

_____ The rider would gallop off alone from St. Joseph.

_____ The rider would ride for one hundred miles.

_____ There the rider got a fresh horse.

_____ A new rider would take over.

Reading for Details
3. Use the clues to answer these questions.

Who started the Pony Express? (paragraph 2) _____

Why was the Pony Express started? (paragraph 1) _____

_____

What was the mail carried in? (paragraph 2) _____

Where was the Pony Express route located? (paragraph 2) _____

_____

When was the Pony Express replaced by the telegraph? (paragraph 3) _____

_____

Reading for Understanding
4. Place the correct letter in the space.

_____ stage coach   a. move mail quickly

_____ Pony Express   b. moved mail slowly

_____ telegraph   c. moved mail over a
                                1,000 miles in 10 days

_____ trucks and planes   d. replaced the Pony
                                Express

The Iroquois—Six as One

About the time that Columbus was just reaching America, five Indian tribes moved from the southeastern United States to the forests in what is now New York. They spoke similar languages and had a way of life that was different from their neighbors. Instead of living in camps and moving around as other Indians did, these people lived in villages in long, bark-covered houses called longhouses. They were farmers, raising corn, beans, and squash. But they were hunters too, killing animals with their favorite weapon, the blowgun.

When European settlers began coming to North America, these tribes – the Seneca, the Oneida, the Mohawks, the Onendaga, and the Cayuga – decided to unite into one great nation. They called themselves the Iroquois, and hoped that by uniting they could keep their land. In 1722, the Tuscarora tribe joined the group, and the Five Nations of the Iroquois became the Six Nations.

During the time the British and French were fighting for control of North America, the Iroquois sided with the British. They were powerful friends and helped the British win that war. But in the end, the Iroquois' friendship with the British was bad for them, for the Iroquois also fought on the British side against the Americans during the Revolutionary War. After the war, the Americans punished the Iroquois for having fought on the British side by sending each tribe to a different part of North America. They were never able to unite again.

Today the Six Nations are still remembered. And their descendants, who still live in the United States and Canada, are proud that their ancestors were once the most powerful people in North America.

Name _____

The Iroquois—
Six as One

Main Idea
1. Choose another title for this story.

_____ Farmers and Hunters

_____ The Iroquois Fight Against the Americans

_____ The Six Nations of the Iroquois

Sequencing
2. Number the events below in the order that they happened.

_____ Five Indian tribes moved to the area that is now New York.

_____ After the Revolutionary War, the Americans punished the Iroquois for siding with the British.

_____ The Tuscarora tribe joined the Iroquois.

_____ The five tribes united into one great nation called the Iroquois.

_____ The Iroquois fought against the Americans in the Revolutionary War.

Reading for Details
3. Use the clues to answer these questions.

What were the names of the five tribes that united? (paragraph 2) _____

_____

When did the sixth tribe join them? (paragraph 2) _____

_____

Why did the tribes unite? (paragraph 2) _____

_____

Where did the Iroquois settle? (paragraph 1) _____

_____

How did the Americans punish the Iroquois? (paragraph 3) _____

_____

Reading for Understanding
4. Place the correct letter in the blank.

_____ blowgun   a. favorite weapon

_____ longhouses   b. last tribe to join the Iroquois nation

_____ Tuscarora   c. friends of the Iroquois

_____ British   d. long, bark-covered houses

The History of Names

A character in a play once asked, "What's in a name?" A name may tell a great deal about you and your family, or it may seem to have no meaning at all. Over thousands of years, people have gotten their names in many different ways.

Parents have always chosen first names for their children. At one time the name usually had a meaning. For example, the name Paul means "small" and Stella means "star." Sometimes a name can look very different in different languages. John, for instance, becomes Ian in Scottish, Jean in French, Jan in Dutch, and Ivan in Russian, but the meaning stays the same.

People have had last names for only about 900 years. When people began to live together in towns, sometimes several people had the same first name. So, if there were two Davids in town, people might call one "David, who is John's son" and the other "David, who is a carpenter." After a few years, the names would become David Johnson and David Carpenter. Other last names came from people's jobs, too. Someone named Smith, or Schmidt, may have been a blacksmith. If your name is Wainwright, one of your ancestors may have made wagons. Other names came from the places people lived. People living near a forest might be called Woods, du Bois, or Wald. In Finland and some other countries, people were always named for the place they lived. So when they moved, their names changed.

No matter what your last name is, it tells something about your ancestors and the way they lived. It is a part of your history.

Name _____

The History of Names

Main Idea

1. Choose another title for this story.

_____ What's In a Name?

_____ The Different Looks of Names

_____ Personal History

Sequencing

2. Number the events below in the order that they happened.

_____ People started using last names.

_____ People began to live together in towns.

_____ Sometimes several people would have the same first name.

_____ People only had first names.

Reading for Details

3. Use the clues to answer these questions.

Who chooses a child's name? (paragraph 2) _____

When did people start using last names? (paragraph 3) _____

_____

How were last names chosen? (paragraph 3) _____

_____

Where does "John" become "Ivan"? (paragraph 2) _____

Why are names important? (paragraph 4) _____

_____

Reading for Understanding

4. Choose the most likely reason for each of these last names.

Kevin Hill

_____ He liked to climb hills.

_____ He was a mountain builder.

_____ He lived on a hill.

Carolyn Baker

_____ She liked to bake bread.

_____ She was the town baker.

_____ She lived by a bakery.

Ben Johnson

_____ He lived near a man named John.

_____ His best friend was named John.

_____ He was the son of John.

JOHN

BEN JOHNSON

Covered Bridges

If you live in a part of the world where there is still a covered bridge, you are lucky. Many of these bridges have been torn down as narrow country roads became modern highways. They are a part of life that is disappearing quickly. But many people wonder, "Why would anyone build a covered bridge in the first place?"

There are many explanations. Some people say that covered bridges kept horses from becoming frightened of the water under them. Other people say that they were shelter for travelers in bad weather. The real reason does have something to do with the weather. But the covers were put up to protect the bridges, not the travelers.

In the eastern United States and Canada, the weather is often rainy in the summer and snowy in the winter. People found that the water and dampness warped their wooden bridges. And even when the bridges were painted, the water got under the paint and rotted the wood. Whole bridges had to be replaced every few years. Finally, someone got the idea of putting a building over the bridge. The bridge was dark like a tunnel, but the cover protected the wood. The idea worked well. Many of the covered bridges left today are well over a hundred years old.

Most of the covered bridges in the United States today are in the New England states of Vermont and New Hampshire and in Ohio. But the honor of having the world's longest covered bridge goes to the Canadian province of New Brunswick. Today, a group of people is working to save the covered bridges that are still left. So in the future, your children and grandchildren will be able to see these beautiful structures.

Name _____

Covered Bridges

Main Idea
1. Choose another title for this story.

_____ Saving an Important Bridge

_____ Tunnels Over Water

_____ The World's Longest Covered Bridge

Sequencing
2. Number the events below in the order that they happened.

_____ The whole bridge would have to be replaced.

_____ The idea worked well, and the covered bridges lasted longer.

_____ People found that water and dampness warped the wood of their bridges.

_____ Someone thought of putting a cover over the bridges.

_____ The covered bridge was invented.

Reading for Details
3. Use the clues to answer these questions.

Where are most of the covered bridges located today? (paragraph 4) _____

_____

Why are people working to save the covered bridges? (paragraph 4) _____

_____

What happened to bridges before covers were added? (paragraph 3) _____

_____

How do covers help the bridges? (paragraph 3) _____

_____

Why have many of the covered bridges disappeared? (paragraph 1) _____

_____

Reading for Understanding
4. Check the other reasons that covered bridges may have been built.

_____ to keep horses from becoming frightened of the water

_____ to make the bridge look pretty

_____ to shelter travelers during bad weather

_____ to give children a place to play "haunted house"

Carving—an Art

Long ago, before people began to paint pictures or write words, someone carved a piece of wood with a bit of sharp stone. When finished, the wood looked like a person, or maybe an animal, and the art of sculpture was born. Other people began to make figures from clay or bone. These were sculptures too.

People at first made sculptures to look like the gods they worshipped. They used the sculptures in religious ceremonies. Later, the Egyptians carved huge statues of their pharoahs, or rulers, out of stone. When the pharoah died, the people put the statue in the pharaoh's tomb. They believed his spirit would return to the statue. Egyptians believed that the statues of animals and gods had life too.

The Greeks and Romans did not believe in statues coming to life. They made sculptures just because they thought sculpture was a beautiful art. Out of a hard white stone, called marble, they carved statues that people love even today. The Greeks are famous for their sculptures of their gods. They used people, usually great athletes, for their models, so the statues look lifelike. Even now, no one has been able to make better sculptures of the human figure.

Today, sculptures are made out of stone, metal, junk, and even food. They may be statues of people or objects or animals. Sometimes only the sculptor who made them knows what they are supposed to be. A new kind of sculpture is soft sculpture, which uses cloth and stuffing to make statues. But no matter what kind of materials sculptors use, they can thank the person thousands of years ago who picked up a stick and a piece of rock and created an art.

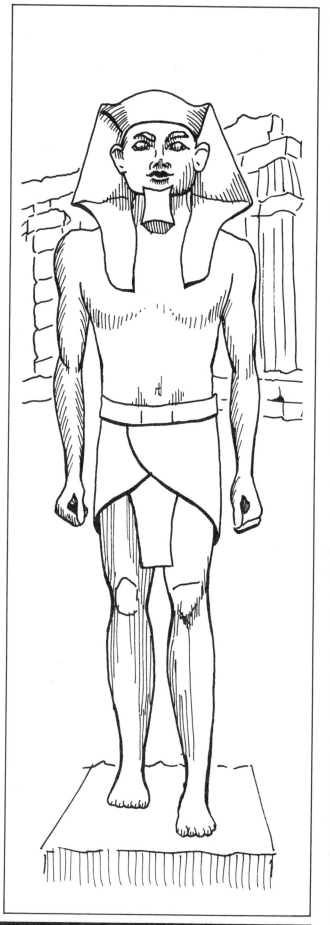

Name _____

Carving—an Art

Main Idea

1. This story tells about

_____ the use of sculpture in religious ceremonies.

_____ a brief history of the art of sculpture.

_____ the Greeks and Romans.

Sequencing

2. Number the events below in the order that they happened.

_____ The Egyptians carved huge sculptures of their pharoahs.

_____ Someone carved a piece of wood with a sharp stone.

_____ Greeks used athletes as models for their sculptures.

_____ People made sculptures to look like the gods they worshipped.

_____ Sculptures were made of stone, metal, or even junk.

Reading for Details

3. Use the clues to answer these questions.

Who carved huge statues of their pharoahs? (paragraph 2) _____

What were the statues made of? (paragraph 2) _____

Where did the Egyptians believe the spirit of the pharoah would return? (paragraph 2)

_____

When did the Egyptians put the statue in the pharoah's tomb? (paragraph 2) _____

_____

Why did the Greeks and Romans make sculptures? (paragraph 3) _____

_____

Reading for Understanding

4. Put these phrases in the correct column.

do not believe in statues coming to life; used athletes as models; use stone, metal, junk, food, cloth; famous for statues of their gods; used marble; only sculptor knows for sure what it is; soft sculpture

Long Ago	Today
_____	_____
_____	_____
_____	_____
_____	_____
_____	_____

The Royal Umbrella

When you have to go out on a rainy day, you probably hunt in your closet for a raincoat and an umbrella. Nobody knows exactly who invented the first umbrella. But this useful gadget has had an exciting history on its way to being just something to keep rain off people's heads.

For a long time, umbrellas weren't used in the rain at all. The people in ancient Egypt and Babylon used them as sunshades when they went outside. Then, over many years, carrying an umbrella became a sign of power and honor. In both Egypt and China, only kings and people of high rank were allowed to use umbrellas. Often, servants would carry the umbrella, holding it over the king's head while he rode along. The common people had to stand in the sun, unprotected. Anyone who dared to own an umbrella would be punished.

The Romans were the first people to use umbrellas as protection from rain. They invented the idea of covering cloth with oil or plant gum to keep rain away. But when the Roman Empire died away, the umbrella disappeared, too. For about a thousand years, there was not one umbrella to be found in Europe. Rich people wore heavy hoods and scarves, while poor people just got wet. Then, around 1600, the umbrella appeared again, in Italy. No one is certain where it came from, but perhaps traders brought umbrellas back from China.

At first, umbrellas were a sign of power again, and only rich people owned them. But by 1700, people all over Europe used umbrellas against the rain. And today, people around the world carry "royal" umbrellas with them whenever they go out on rainy days.

The Royal Umbrella

Main Idea

1. This story tells about

_____ the history of the umbrella.

_____ using an umbrella on a rainy day.

_____ a sign of power.

Sequencing

2. Number the events below in the order that they happened.

_____ The Romans used umbrellas as protection from rain.

_____ People in ancient Egypt used umbrellas as sunshades.

_____ People all over Europe used umbrellas.

_____ The umbrella disappeared.

_____ Rich Europeans started using umbrellas.

Reading for Details

3. Use the clues to answer these questions.

Who invented the umbrella? (paragraph 1) _____

_____

What happened to common people in Egypt who used umbrellas? (paragraph 2) _____

_____

When did the umbrella disappear? (paragraph 3) _____

_____

Where and when did the umbrella reappear? (paragraph 3) _____

_____

Why are umbrellas used today? (paragraph 4) _____

_____

Reading for Understanding

4. Check the correct statements.

_____ At first I was used for protection from shadows.

_____ The Romans were the first ones to use me as protection from the rain.

_____ Only poor people could use me.

_____ I was "water-proofed" by covering cloth with oil or plant gum.

_____ Anyone can use me now.

The Fighting Spiders of Japan

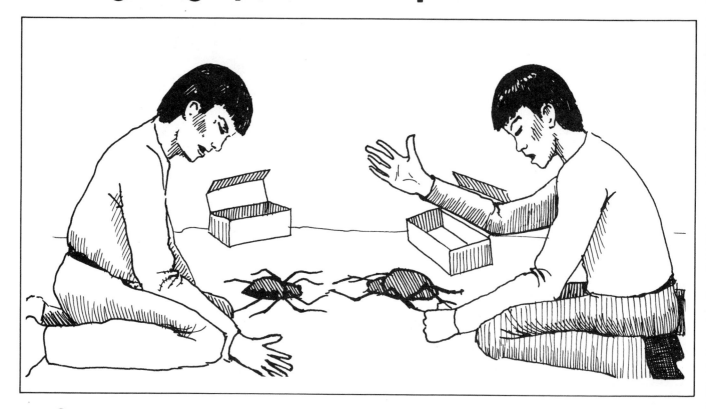

On summer mornings in China and Japan, many boys get up early. Carrying small boxes, they go outside and search in gardens and bushes. Each boy is looking for just the right spider web. And in that web he hopes will be the best fighting spider in the world.

Spider contests are as popular in China and Japan as marble games are in North America. Only male spiders are used for the contests, and a good strong spider is his owner's pride and joy. Every day, a group of boys gathers in the playground or at someone's house. Then out come the spider boxes, and the contest begins. Two of the boys put their spiders on a table. When the spiders see each other, they become angry. They threaten each other and fight until one of the spiders gives up or runs away. After two fights, the winners meet each other to see which will be the champion. The boys cheer for their spiders and promise them fine new homes if they win. The winner is named king of the spiders, and his owner takes special care of him because he has won a great honor. At last, his owner lets him go free as a reward. Then another spider has a chance to become king.

In Japan, grown men keep fighting spiders too. In one town, two men have raised spiders for many years, and each year they have a contest to see who has the best spider for the year. The owner of the champion spider wins a prize, but people only tease the loser. Spider contests may seem unusual, but they are a tradition that has been passed down from fathers to sons for hundreds of years.

Name _____

The Fighting Spiders of Japan

Main Idea

1. This story tells about

_____ the popular game of spider fights in China and Japan.

_____ Chinese and Japanese boys at play.

_____ male spiders fighting.

Sequencing

2. Number the events below in order.

_____ Two boys put their spiders on the table.

_____ The winner is named king of the spiders.

_____ A group of boys gather in the playground.

_____ The spiders see each other and become angry.

_____ The owner of the winning spider lets him go free.

Reading for Details

3. Use the clues to answer these questions.

Who takes part in the spider contests? (paragraph 1 & 3) _____

_____

How do the boys find their spiders? (paragraph 1) _____

_____

Where do the boys gather for the contests? (paragraph 2) _____

_____

When do the spiders become angry? (paragraph 2) _____

_____

Why does the owner let the winning spider go free? (paragraph 2) _____

_____

Reading for Understanding

4. Choose the topic for each paragraph.

Paragraph 1	Paragraph 2	Paragraph 3
_____ getting up	_____ king spiders	_____ two men
_____ gardening	_____ spider contests	_____ a town
_____ looking for fighting spiders	_____ cheers for the winner	_____ a Japanese tradition

The Magic Stones

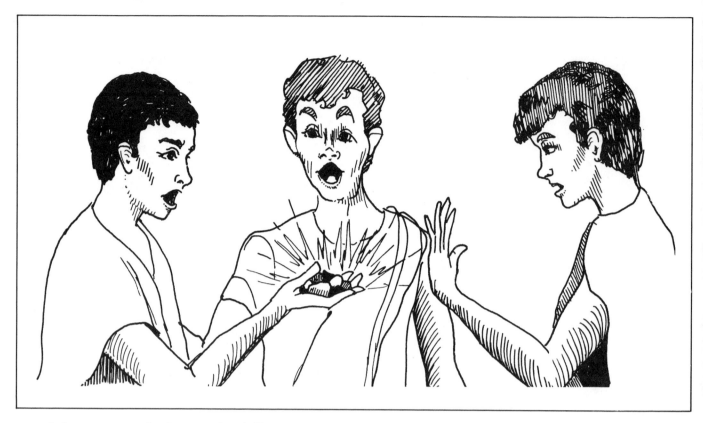

Many people in ancient times believed that precious stones had mysterious powers. For instance, diamonds were supposed to keep people from having nightmares. And wearing amethyst, a purple stone, was said to cure a headache or toothache. Today when people wear their birthstones, they are carrying on an old idea that certain stones have special powers.

There are twelve birthstones, one for each month of the year. For example, people born in May often wear their birthstone, the emerald. Turquoise is the birthstone for December, and the ruby is the birthstone for people born in July. March's birthstone is the aquamarine, and August's is the peridot.

Every birthstone stands for something special, and people are said to be like their birthstones. People born in October are lucky. They are the only people who can safely wear their birthstone, the opal. Opals are supposed to be unlucky for anyone else to wear. Pearls stand for goodness, so people born in June are supposed to be especially good-tempered. Garnets are red, and they stand for strength. So people born in January are supposed to be strong and not easily hurt. Anyone who wears a topaz, the November birthstone, is said to be a good friend. The sapphire is the September birthstone, and it stands for clear thinking. All the other months' birthstones have special meanings too.

Today, not many people believe that these stones have special powers, and we wear them just because we think they are beautiful. But wearing birthstones is fun, and sometimes it's nice to pretend they're magic.

Name _____

The Magic Stones

Main Idea

1. This story tells about

   _____ mysterious powers.

   _____ birthstones.

   _____ months of the year.

Sequencing

2. Number the events below in the order that you read about them.

   _____ Ancient people believed precious stones had mysterious powers.

   _____ Amethyst was said to cure a headache.

   _____ Diamonds were said to prevent nightmares.

   _____ People wearing birthstones are carrying on the idea that certain stones have special powers.

Reading for Details

3. Use the clues to answer these questions.

   Who believed that precious stones had mysterious powers? (paragraph 1) _____

   _____

   When are people carrying on that idea? (paragraph 1) _____

   _____

   What is an amethyst? (paragraph 1) _____

   What is the birthstone of May? (paragraph 2) _____

   Why do people wear their birthstones today? (paragraph 4) _____

   _____

Reading for Understanding

4. Place the correct letter in the blank.

   _____ topaz   a. stands for clear thinking

   _____ pearl   b. stands for strength

   _____ sapphire   c. said to be lucky for only those born in October

   _____ garnet   d. means a good friend

   _____ opal   e. stands for goodness

The Mysteries of Chaco Canyon

Once, almost a thousand years ago, a tribe of Pueblo Indians lived in Chaco Canyon in northern New Mexico. A river flowed through the canyon, and the people planted corn and squash in the rich soil by the river. They were peaceful people who only wanted to grow their crops and be left alone.

Today there is no river in Chaco Canyon, and the earth is dry and brown. No one knows what happened to the people of Chaco Canyon. Maybe the river dried up and they moved away. Maybe they were driven away by another tribe. But on the walls of the canyon is a very important clue to understanding the Chaco people.

Some people were climbing the Chaco Canyon walls one day when they found something strange. Carved in the rock was a giant spiral shape. Two smaller spiral shapes were carved beside it. The climbers were puzzled. Perhaps the spirals were a decoration, but there were no carvings anywhere else in the whole canyon. Then someone noticed that the sunlight from a narrow crack in some rocks made a line on the big spiral. The people came back day after day. Finally they found that on the longest day of the year, the line of light crossed the exact center of the spiral. Later, they discovered that on the shortest day of the year, the light just touched the outside of the spiral. The big spiral was a calendar that the Chaco people had carved to tell them the months of the year!

The two small spirals are still a mystery. But people are studying them even today, and one day someone will discover more secrets of the mysterious Chaco people.

Name _____

The Mysteries of Chaco Canyon

Main Idea

1. Choose another title for this story.

_____ The Mysterious Calendar

_____ The Hiking Trip

_____ Life in Chaco Canyon

Sequencing

2. Number the events below in the order that they happened.

_____ It was decided that the big spiral was used as a calendar.

_____ They discovered the spiral shapes on the wall.

_____ Some people were climbing the canyon walls.

_____ They noticed that the sunlight made a line on the big spiral.

_____ The two small spirals are still being studied.

Reading for Details

3. Use the clues to answer these questions.

Who lived in Chaco Canyon 1,000 years ago? (paragraph 1) _____

What was found on their canyon walls? (paragraph 3) _____

Where did the sunlight shining on the big spiral come from? (paragraph 3) _____

_____

When does the line of light just touch the outside of the spiral? (paragraph 3) _____

_____

When does it touch the exact center of the spiral? (paragraph 3) _____

_____

Why are the spirals studied today? (paragraph 4) _____

Reading for Understanding

4. Circle Yes or No.

I am a member of the Navajo Tribe.	Yes	No
I lived in southern Mexico in the Chaco Canyon.	Yes	No
I lived by a river.	Yes	No
I grew corn and strawberries.	Yes	No
I was a peaceful person.	Yes	No
I made a calendar on the canyon walls.	Yes	No

The Story of Spinning

Today, when we want new clothes, we can go to a clothing store and buy whatever we like. But for people two or three hundred years ago, getting new clothing was not so easy. Not only did they make their own clothing, but sometimes people wove their own cloth at home. And if they owned their own sheep, they even spun the wool into yarn themselves.

Wool cannot just be taken from the sheep and spun. First it must be cleaned and then carded. In a large family, carding was usually the children's job, because it is easy but tiresome. Carding is done with two wide combs that have rows of steel teeth. The person carding puts a piece of wool on one comb, then pulls the other comb across the wool again and again. This combing makes the wool fibers straight and smooth so they can be spun.

Finally the mother or older sister of the family could use the wool for spinning. Spinning just means twisting and stretching the fibers into yarn. You have spun yarn if you have ever pulled and twisted a cotton ball into a long string. Usually, though, a spinning wheel helps make the pulling and twisting easier. The spinner holds the wool in her hands and twists one end onto the yarn already on the spindle, or long winding stick. The spinning wheel turns the spindle, pulling the wool into yarn and winding it onto the spindle at the same time. Finally, the yarn is ready for weaving.

Today, machines can spin yarn much faster than people can. But in some places, people still make their own yarn because they love the old art of spinning.

Name _____

The Story of Spinning

Main Idea

1. This story explains

_____ the art of sheering sheep.

_____ the art of spinning.

_____ the art of making clothes.

Sequencing

2. Number the events below in the order that they happen.

_____ The spinning wheel pulls the wool into yarn.

_____ The wool is taken from the sheep.

_____ The wool must be cleaned and then carded.

_____ The yarn is ready for weaving.

_____ The cloth is used to make clothing for the family.

Reading for Details

3. Use the clues to answer these questions.

Who usually carded the wool? (paragraph 2) _____

Why did they usually get that job? (paragraph 2) _____

_____

What tool was used for carding? (paragraph 2) _____

_____

When was the wool ready for weaving? (paragraph 3) _____

_____

Why do some people still spin their own yarn? (paragraph 4) _____

_____

Reading for Understanding

4. Place the correct letter in the blank.

_____ carding   a. makes wool fibers straight and smooth

_____ combing   b. twisting and stretching the fibers into yarn

_____ spinning   c. long winding stick

_____ spindle   d. easy but tiresome

Answer Key

The Fairy Ring

Main Idea
1. Choose another title for the story.

_X_ A Magical Dance

_____ Shon Becomes a Grandfather

_____ A Circle of Mushrooms

Sequencing
2. Number the events below in the order that they happened.

_2_ He stepped inside the fairy ring

_1_ Shon heard the fairy music.

_4_ He ran back to his home and knocked on the door.

_3_ He escaped from the fairy ring.

_5_ Shon discovered he had become a very old man.

Reading for Details
3. Use the clues to answer the questions.

Who calls a circle of mushrooms a "fairy ring"? (paragraph 1) people in England

When do the fairies come out of the forest? (paragraph 2) when the moon shines

What do people follow to the fairy ring? (paragraph 2) sound of music

Where did Shon run as soon as he escaped from the fairy ring? (paragraph 3) home

Why was Shon a very old man at the end of the story? (paragraph 7) He had spent many years dancing in the fairy ring.

Reading for Understanding
4. Circle yes or no.

People say that I play music on whistles and drums. Yes **No**

People say that I dance all night long. **Yes** No

People say that one of my minutes is the same as seven of your years. **Yes** No

Page 3

The Foolish Coyote

Main Idea
1. What is the main idea of this story?

_X_ The coyote wanted to be king.

_____ The coyote was a hunter.

_____ The blackbirds tricked the coyote.

Sequencing
2. Number the events below in the order that they happened.

_3_ The blackbirds stuck feathers into the coyote.

_5_ The coyote crashed to the ground.

_2_ He asked the blackbirds to teach him how to fly.

_1_ The coyote was hunting on the mountain.

_4_ The coyote jumped off the mountain and seemed to fly.

Reading for Details
3. Use the clues to answer the questions.

When did the blackbirds gather on top of the mountain? (paragraph 1) in the fall

Where did each blackbird pull a feather from? (paragraph 4) from its wing

Why did the blackbirds say they would help the coyote? (paragraph 3) to have some fun

Reading for Understanding
4. Write the word or phrase, that is used in the story.

How did the blackbirds fly and dance? beautifully

How did the coyote feel when he ran to the edge of the mountain? excited

How did the coyote land on the ground? with a crash

Page 5

A Boy Named Maul

Main Idea
1. Choose another title for this story.

_____ The Fight of the Five Brothers

_____ A Gift of an Island

_X_ How New Zealand Was Made

Sequencing
2. Number the events below in the order that they happened.

_3_ Maui caught an island with his magic hook.

_1_ Maui's brothers made plans to shame him.

_4_ Maui gave the island to his people.

_2_ All the brothers went fishing.

Reading for Details
3. Use the clues to answer the questions.

Besides Maui, who did all the work? (paragraph 1) his mother

What didn't Maui's brothers know about him? (paragraph 3) Maui had magic powers.

When did the brothers want to be king? (paragraph 4) when they saw the beautiful island

Where did the sea god live? (paragraph 4) on the island

Why did Maui give the island to his people? (paragraph 5) He did not want to be king.

Reading for Understanding
4. List the word(s) that describe the character in the correct column.

magical generous   lazy jealous   hard-working plays favorites   kind smart

Maui	Brothers	Mother	Sea God
magical generous kind smart	lazy jealous	hard-working plays favorites	generous

Page 7

The Monkey and the Ogre

Main Idea
1. Choose another title for this story.

_____ The Terrible Ogre

_X_ How the Wise Monkey Defeated The Ogre

_____ A Magic Forest

Sequencing
2. Number the events in the order that they happened.

_1_ The wise monkey waited by the lake for the ogre.

_4_ The ogre disappeared with a roar.

_3_ The monkeys drank the water through hollow reeds.

_2_ The ogre said he would eat all the monkeys.

Reading for Details
3. Use the clues to answer the questions.

Where was the magic forest? (paragraph 1) India

What lived in the middle of the lake? (paragraph 1) an ogre

When did the ogre jump out of the lake? (paragraph 1) whenever any animal tried to drink from the lake

Who knew about the ogre? (paragraph 2) the wise old monkey

Why did the monkeys use long, hollow reeds? (paragraph 7) to stay away from the lake and still be able to drink

Reading for Understanding
4. The monkey was able to outsmart the ogre because

_X_ he thought before he acted.

_____ he was stronger than the ogre.

_____ the ogre wasn't watching.

Page 9

Myths, Legends, Neat Things IF8713

© 1990 Instructional Fair, Inc.

Answer Key

When the Sun Went Away

Sequencing

1. Number the events below in the order that they happened.

   1 The god of night put a snake around his sister's chair.

   4 The sun goddess became curious and crept out of the cave.

   3 People gathered at the mouth of the cave and made noise.

   2 The sun goddess ran into the cave and would not come out.

Reading for Details

2. Use the clues to answer the questions.

   Who gathered at the cave? (paragraph 6) _the people_

   What did they do there? (paragraph 6) _Beat drums, rang bells, sang_

   When did they grab the goddess' hand? (paragraph 6) _when they saw her_

   Why did they dance for joy? (paragraph 6) _The earth became bright again._

Main Idea

3. What is the main idea of the last paragraph of this story?

   _____ The sun goddess came to the mouth of the cave.

   _____ The sun god promised not to trick his sister again.

   __X__ The people were able to bring the sun goddess out of the cave.

Reading for Understanding

4. The people loved the sun goddess because _she made the crops grow and the trees bloom._

5. The people feared the god of night because _he brought evil spirits to harm the land._

Page 11

How People Were Made— A South American Legend

Main Idea

1. What is the main idea of this story?

   _____ The animals were smarter than the gods.

   _____ The gods were happy when they made plants and animals.

   __X__ The animals helped the gods to make people.

Sequencing

2. Number the events below in the order that they happened.

   4 The gods made people from the leaves of a magic tree.

   2 The gods made plants and animals.

   1 The gods made the earth of rock and water.

   3 The gods made people from mud.

Reading for Details

3. Use the clues to answer the questions.

   Who made the earth? (paragraph 1) _the gods_

   What kinds of noises did the animals make? (paragraph 2) _mooed, barked, hissed, roared_

   Where did the animals take the gods? (paragraph 6) _into the forest_

   When did the people begin to speak? (paragraph 6) _as soon as they were made_

   Why did the gods make people? (paragraph 3) _to speak their names and honor them_

Reading for Understanding

4. Write happy or unhappy.

   When the gods made the earth of rock and water, they were _____

   When the gods made plants and animals on Earth, they were _____

   When the animals could not speak the gods names, the gods were _____

   When the people began to speak the gods names, the gods were _____

Page 13

Tony Beaver and the Watermelons

Main Idea

1. This story is about

   __X__ a farmer who couldn't get his watermelons to market.

   _____ a man who loved to eat.

   _____ a man who couldn't swim.

Sequencing

2. Number the events below in the order that they happened.

   2 He hoed and weeded and worked in the fields.

   3 The watermelons grew to be as big as barns.

   4 Tony tried to take the watermelons to market.

   1 Tony bought some land and planted watermelon seeds.

Reading for Details

3. Use the clues to answer the questions.

   Who tells the story about Tony? (paragraph 1) _people in W. Virginia_

   Where could people hide? (paragraph 1) _in his shoe prints in the mud_

   What was Tony taller than? (paragraph 1) _a house_

   Why did Tony decide to become a farmer? (paragraph 1) _to grow food_

   When were the watermelons as big as barns? (paragraph 2) _by harvest time_

Reading for Understanding

4. Check the best answer(s).

   What do you think Tony might do when he gets to Ohio?

   __X__ become a farmer again

   _____ build a house on a straight road

   _____ learn to swim

Page 15

How the Chipmunk Got His Stripes

Main Idea

1. Choose another title for this story.

   _____ The Great Bear

   _____ The Selfish Squirrels

   __X__ How the Bear Helped the Chipmunk

Sequencing

2. Number the events below in the order that they happened.

   1 The squirrels laughed at the chipmunk.

   3 A bear clawed the chipmunk's back.

   2 The chipmunk crept away into the forest.

   4 The claw marks became stripes.

   5 The squirrels made the chipmunk king of the animals.

Reading for Details

3. Use the clues to answer the questions.

   Who told this story a long time ago? (paragraph 1) _the Indians_

   What wouldn't the squirrels share? (paragraph 3) _their chestnuts_

   Where did the chipmunk run for safety? (paragraph 7) _a hole_

   Why was the chipmunk happy in the end? (paragraph 9) _He had all the nuts he could eat, and the animals never laughed at him again._

Reading for Understanding

4. Write the correct word or phrase.

   I was sad and hungry when _I hid in the forest_

   I was scared when _the bear trapped me_

   I thought fast when _the bear was about to eat me._

Page 17

Answer Key

The Unicorn

Main Idea
1. Choose another title for this story.
   - [X] A Strange and Magical Animal
   - [ ] A Beautiful Girl in the Forest
   - [ ] How to Hunt a Unicorn

Sequencing
2. Number the events below in order.
   - 2 She would walk until she came to a pond.
   - 4 The unicorn would see the girl and fall in love with her.
   - 3 If she sat down by the pond, a unicorn would come.
   - 1 A beautiful girl would go into the forest.
   - 5 The unicorn would lay its head on her lap.

Reading for Details
3. Use the clues to answer the questions.

Who saw a unicorn? (paragraph 1) __no one__

What gave the unicorn its name? (paragraph 1) __its one horn__

Why did people hunt unicorns? (paragraph 2) __to bring good luck; the horn was supposed to find poison and cure sickness__

Where did people go to hunt the unicorn? (paragraph 2) __in the forests__

When would the unicorn fall in love with the girl? (paragraph 3) __when he saw her__

Reading for Understanding
4. Why did I let the beautiful girl catch me?
   - [ ] She gave me food.
   - [ ] She gave me a place to live.
   - [X] She was kind and gentle to me.

Page 19

The Story of Arachne

Main Idea
1. Long ago people made up myths to explain why things happened. What does this story explain?
   - [ ] why cloth is woven
   - [ ] why Arachne was not rich and beautiful
   - [X] why brown spiders weave fine webs

Sequencing
2. Number the events below in the order that they happened.
   - 2 Arachne wove a cloth that looked like gold and jewels.
   - 5 Arachne shrank until she became a tiny brown spider.
   - 4 Minerva sprinkled magic water on Arachne.
   - 1 Minerva challenged Arachne to a contest.
   - 3 Minerva saw that Arachne's cloth was as good as hers.

Reading for Details
3. Use the clues to answer the questions.

Where did Minerva find Arachne? (paragraph 4) __in her house__

Who agreed to the weaving contest? (paragraph 5) __Arachne__

What did Minerva do when Arachne won the contest? (paragraph 6) __flew into a rage & turned her into a spider__

When did Arachne begin to shrink? (paragraph 6) __when Minerva sprinkled magic water on her__

Reading for Understanding
4. Scan paragraph 5 and answer these questions.

What phrases are used to describe the cloth that the goddess wove? __all the colors of the rainbow; sparkled in the sun; like a butterfly__

What phrases are used to describe the cloth that Arachne wove? __looked like gold and jewels; dazzled the eyes__

Draw a picture of each piece of cloth.

Page 21

The Wise Men and the Sensible Man

Main Idea
1. This story tells about
   - [X] a man whose life was saved because he was both smart and sensible.
   - [ ] four men who took a walk.
   - [ ] bones that came alive.

Sequencing
2. Number the events in the order that they happened.
   - 3 The wise men made the bones come alive.
   - 1 The four men went for a walk.
   - 4 Hari went home alive.
   - 2 The men came upon the bones of a lion.

Reading for Details
3. Use the clues to answer the questions.

Who didn't the villagers listen to? (paragraph 1) __Hari__

Where did the men go on their walk? (paragraph 2) __outside the village__

What did the men find on their walk? (paragraph 3) __bones of a lion__

Why did Hari tell the other men not to be foolish? (paragraph 4) __because the lion would kill them when brought back to life.__

When did Hari go home? (paragraph 6) __after the lion was gone__

Reading for Understanding
4. To have common sense means to have
   - [ ] lots of money.
   - [ ] ordinary judgement.
   - [X] good judgement.

To be wise means
   - [X] having information.
   - [ ] being old.
   - [ ] having a big head.

Page 23

The First Incas

Main Idea
1. Choose another title for this story.
   - [ ] The Sun God and the Moon Goddess
   - [ ] A Story About the Andes Mountains
   - [X] How Peace Came to the Incas

Sequencing
2. Number the events in the order that they happened.
   - 2 The sun god and the moon goddess felt sorry for the miserable people.
   - 4 The people lived in peace, made one nation, and called themselves the Incas.
   - 1 Thousands of years ago, people who lived in the Andes Mountains of South America were poor and miserable.
   - 3 The sun god and the moon goddess sent their children to help the people.

Reading for Details
3. Use the clues to answer the questions.

Where did the sun god and the moon goddess live? (paragraph 2) __in the sky__

When did the son and daughter start to help the people? (paragraph 3) __when they were old enough__

Why did the son think the people were miserable? (paragraph 4) __because they were always fighting each other__

What does "Incas" mean? (paragraph 5) __king's tribe.__

Reading for Understanding
4. Match the characters with the best adjective for each one by writing the correct letter.
   - a. Sun God — __d__ peaceful
   - b. Son — __b__ proud
   - c. Moon Goddess — __a__ generous
   - d. Incas — __c__ sad

Page 25

Answer Key

The Knockers of Cornwall

Main Idea
1. Choose the main idea of paragraph 4.
   ___ The knockers' bells jingle.
   _X_ The knockers love to tease the miners.
   ___ The knockers dance at night.

Sequencing
2. Number the events in the order you learned about them.
   _4_ The miners give the knockers food.
   _1_ The knockers knock and tap by veins of metal.
   _3_ The knockers want to get paid.
   _2_ The miners find the veins of tin.

Reading for Details
3. Use the clues to answer the questions.
   Who said that knockers live in mines? (paragraph 1) _miners in Cornwall, England_
   Where are the mines located? (paragraph 1) _Cornwall, England_
   When do the miners know there is ore nearby? (paragraph 2) _when they hear the sounds of the knockers' hammers_
   What do the knockers demand for payment? (paragraph 3) _food_
   Why do the knockers throw stones? (paragraph 3) _to stop miners from whistling and swearing_

Reading for Understanding
4. We have things that we like and do not like. Put them in the right column.

people, helping, money, whistling, music, red suits, food, gold, teasing, bells dancing, yellow scarves, swearing

like	do not like
people, helping, red suits, food, teasing, bells, dancing, yellow scarves, music	money whistling swearing gold

Selling the Sheepskin

Main Idea
1. Choose another title for this story.
   ___ The Trip to the Market
   ___ A Wise Father
   _X_ A Test for a Son

Sequencing
2. Number the events in the order that they happened.
   _4_ The boy told the magician his problem.
   _3_ The boy was ashamed to go home.
   _1_ The boy took the sheepskin to the market to sell.
   _2_ People in the market laughed at the boy.

Reading for Details
3. Use the clues to answer the questions.
   When did the story take place? (paragraph 1) _many years ago_
   Why did the boy go to the market? (paragraph 1) _to sell the sheepskin_
   Who told the boy how to solve his problem? (paragraph 3) _the magician_
   What did the girl pay for? (paragraph 5) _the wool_
   Where did the boy search for the girl? (paragraph 6) _the countryside_

Reading for Understanding
4. Check the best answer.
   The test showed that
   ___ the boy was wiser than his father.
   ___ the father was wiser than the boy.
   ___ the magician was wiser than both the father and the boy.
   _X_ the girl was wisest of all.

The Indian Girl and the Serpent God

Main Idea
1. This story tells about
   _X_ an Indian girl who meets a handsome man.
   ___ an Indian girl with a strange habit.
   ___ a serpent god who is unhappy.

Sequencing
2. Number the events in the order that they happened.
   _2_ The serpent god said that the girl had to go with him.
   _3_ The serpent god became a handsome young man.
   _1_ The girl went to the stream to wash clothes.
   _4_ The girl followed the young man under the water.

Reading for Details
3. Use the clues to answer the questions.
   Who did the Indian girl live with? (paragraph 1) _her family_
   Where did the Indian girl wash her clothes? (paragraph 1) _in the stream_
   When did the snake god come out of the water? (paragraph 2) _when the girl went to the stream_
   What did the Indian girl wear on her journey? (paragraph 3) _her best clothes and jewelry_
   Why did the Indian girl forget she was sad? (paragraph 1) _The serpent god had become a handsome young man._

Reading for Understanding
4. For each adjective listed, write the letter of the character it describes.
   a. Indian girl
   b. Serpent god
   c. Young man

   _a_ beautiful   _a_ lovely
   _a_ terrified   _a_ sad
   _c_ handsome   _b_ angry
   _b_ terrible   _c_ kind
   _a_ good   _a_ glad
   _a_ hungry

Phaeton and the Chariot of the Sun

Main Idea
1. Choose the main idea of paragraph 5.
   ___ The lakes dried up.
   _X_ Phaeton could not control the horses.
   ___ The horses left the path and burned the earth.

Sequencing
2. Number the events below in the order that they happened.
   _1_ Phaeton climbed Mt. Olympus to visit his father.
   _3_ Phaeton begged Apollo to let him drive the sun chariot.
   _5_ Zeus turned Phaeton into a shooting star.
   _2_ Apollo showed Phaeton the horses of the sun.
   _4_ Phaeton let the reins drop, and the horses left the path.

Reading for Details
3. Use the clues to answer the questions.
   Where did Phaeton live? (paragraph 1) _Greece_
   What did Phaeton climb into? (paragraph 5) _the chariot_
   When did the horses leave the path? (paragraph 5) _when Phaeton dropped the reins_
   Who was Zeus? (paragraph 6) _the chief god_
   Why did Zeus turn Phaeton into a shooting star? (paragraph 6) _because he could not let the earth burn_

Reading for Understanding
4. Check the best answer.
   When Phaeton climbed into the chariot, he felt
   _X_ excited   ___ unsure   ___ scared
   When Apollo first saw Phaeton, he felt
   ___ indifferent ___ sad   _X_ joyful
   How did Zeus feel about turning Phaeton into a shooting star?
   ___ unconcerned ___ happy   _X_ sad

Answer Key

The Beginning of Good and Evil

Main Idea
1. Choose another title for this story.

_____ A Story from Norway and Sweden

__X__ The Struggle Between Good and Evil

_____ Two Frost Giants

Sequencing
2. Number the events in the order that they happened.

__3__ Odin killed Ymir and most of his children.

__5__ The frost giants tried to make trouble.

__1__ Buri and Ymir came out of the ice.

__4__ Odin made Midgard and Asgard.

__2__ Buri and Ymir had many children.

Reading for Details
3. Use the clues to answer the questions.

Who said there was no world in the beginning? (paragraph 1) *people in Norway and Sweden*

What was in the north? (paragraph 1) *frozen darkness*

Where was the burning fire? (paragraph 1) *in the south*

Why did Odin make Midgard? (paragraph 5) *for people to live in*

When did the frost giants make trouble for the people and the gods? (paragraph 6) *whenever they could to this day*

Reading for Understanding
4. Write the letter in the correct space.

a. Odin ___d___ a rainbow bridge

b. Midgard ___a___ father of the gods

c. Asgard ___b___ the world

d. Bifrost ___c___ place for the gods

e. Ymir ___f___ father of everything good and beautiful

f. Buri ___e___ father of everything evil and ugly

Page 35

The Story of Zan

Main Idea
1. Choose the main idea of paragraph 2.

__X__ Zan became a strong, kind man and rewarded his animal friends.

_____ Zan put his toys in a secret cave.

_____ Zan made hives for the bees.

Sequencing
2. Number the events in the order that they happened.

__2__ Animals gave gifts to Zan.

__1__ The Earth Mother had a child named Zan.

__3__ Zan rewarded his animal friends.

__5__ Zan turned the men into birds.

__4__ Three evil men tried to steal Zan's toys.

Reading for Details
3. Use the clues to answer the questions.

Where was Zan born? (paragraph 1) *island of Crete*

Who gave the milk to Zan? (paragraph 1) *wild goats*

When did Zan reward his animal friends? (paragraph 2) *when he grew up into a strong, kind man*

Why did Zan let the evil men live? (paragraph 4) *They were in the cave of life.*

What did Zan turn the men into? (paragraph 5) *birds*

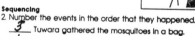

Reading for Understanding
4. Long ago people made up stories to explain why things happened.

What does this story explain?

_____ why goats give milk

__X__ why no one can understand birds

_____ why no one can be killed in the cave of life

Page 37

The Loup-Garou

Main Idea
1. Choose another title for this story.

_____ How to Escape a Loup-Garou's Trap

_____ A Witch's Spell

__X__ The French Werewolf

Sequencing
2. Number the events in the order that they happened.

__3__ A drop of blood would fall.

__1__ A loup-garou would trap its victim.

__4__ The animal skin would fall to the ground.

__2__ To escape, the victim would cut the loup-garou.

__5__ The person who had been a loup-garou would come out.

Reading for Details
3. Use the clues to answer the questions.

Who told the legends of the werewolves? (paragraph 1) *French-speaking people of North America*

Why did French mothers tell their children that a loup-garou might get them? (paragraph 1) *to make them behave*

What kind of animals can the people turn into? (paragraph 1) *wolves, bears, dogs, oxen, pigs*

Where might the loup-garou throw bad magic? (paragraph 3) *at a person's house*

When would the animal skin fall to the ground? (paragraph 4) *as soon as a drop of blood fell*

Reading for Understanding
4. Check the correct statements.

__X__ I became a loup-garou by making an agreement with the devil.

_____ I have to work for a witch for six months.

_____ It is easy to get away from me.

__X__ I trap a person by tripping him.

Page 39

Tuwara and the Mosquitoes

Main Idea
1. Choose another title for this story.

_____ The Little Singers

_____ An Island in the Pacific

__X__ How the King Rid His Island of Mosquitoes

Sequencing
2. Number the events in the order that they happened.

__3__ Tuwara gathered the mosquitoes in a bag.

__1__ The people begged Tuwara to get rid of the mosquitoes.

__4__ Tuwara gave the mosquitoes to the king.

__2__ Tuwara invited the king to his island.

__5__ Tuwara's island had no mosquitoes.

Reading for Details
3. Use the clues to answer the questions.

Why did the people love Tuwara? (paragraph 1) *because he was kind and wise*

What did the mosquitoes do that bothered the people? (paragraph 1) *They bit the people.*

Where did Tuwara go? (paragraph 2) *to a nearby island*

When did Tuwara take the king into the hut? (paragraph 4) *when night came*

Who were the little people? (paragraph 6) *the mosquitoes*

Reading for Understanding
4. Choose another solution for Tuwara's problem.

_____ cast a spell on the mosquitoes so they would not be able to buzz or bite

_____ move his people to a different island

__X__ gather the mosquitoes in a bag and sink it in the ocean

Page 41

Answer Key

The Tiny Fliers

Main Idea
1. Choose another title for this story.
____ Flying Flowers
____ Sixty Meals a Day
_X_ King of the Fliers

Sequencing
2. Number the events below in the order that they happen.
_4_ They suck the nectar from flowers.
_2_ Hummingbirds look for flowers.
_1_ Flying makes hummingbirds hungry.
_3_ They make their long tongues into tubes.

Reading for Details
3. Use the clues to answer these questions.
What is the smallest bird of all? (paragraph 1) *the hummingbird*
Where do all the different kinds of hummingbirds live? (paragraph 2) *North and South America*
When do hummingbirds look just like flowers? (paragraph 2) *when they fly around flowers*
Why do hummingbirds eat all the time? (paragraph 4) *to get energy for flying*

Reading for Understanding
4. Check the correct answer(s).
I am king of the flowers because
_X_ I can hover and fly back-wards.
____ I can fly upside down.
I am king of the eaters because
____ I can make my tongue work like a straw.
_X_ I eat 60 meals a day.
I was named a hummingbird because
_X_ my wings beat so fast that they make the air hum.
____ I look like a flower.

The Big Bird with the Big Bill

Main Idea
1. This story tells about
____ an old rhyme.
____ a dirty and unsafe Gulf of Mexico.
_X_ two kinds of pelicans.

Sequencing
2. Number the events below in the order that they happen.
_2_ When they see fish, they land on the water and form a half-circle.
_3_ They beat their wings on the water to make the fish swim to the middle of the circle.
_4_ They eat the fish.
_1_ White pelicans fly together high above the water.

Reading for Details
3. Use the clues to answer these questions.
Who was right about the pelican? (paragraph 1) *the person who wrote the rhyme*
What part of a pelican will hold three gallons of water? (paragraph 1) *the pouch*
Where is the home of pelicans? (paragraph 2) *North America*
When does a brown pelican dive into the water and scoop up a fish in its bill? (paragraph 3) *when it sees the fish*
Why did brown pelicans become endangered? (paragraph 5) *dirty, unsafe water in the Gulf of Mexico*

Reading for Understanding
4. Put these phrases in the right column.
lives around lakes in the western United States, lives near the ocean and the Gulf of Mexico, weighs 20 pounds, 5 feet long, weighs 10 pounds, shorter than 5 feet, fishes alone, fishes together, beats wings and frightens fish into a circle, almost died out, bill can hold more than its belly

Brown Pelican *lives near the ocean and the Gulf of Mexico, weighs 10 lbs, shorter than 5', eats fish, fishes alone, almost died out, bill holds more than belly*

White Pelican *lives around lakes in the western U.S. weighs 20 lbs, 5' long, eats fish, fish together, beats wings and frightens fish into a circle, bill holds more than belly*

The Ice of Summer

Main Idea
1. This story explains
____ rainstorms.
____ thunder and lightning.
_X_ hailstorms.

Sequencing
2. Number the events below in the order that they happen.
_4_ The hailstone becomes heavy and falls to the ground.
_3_ When more raindrops freeze on the frozen raindrop, it gets bigger.
_1_ A raindrop falls through cold air and freezes.
_2_ Wind carries the frozen raindrop back up to the warm air.

Reading for Details
3. Use the clues to answer these questions.
What are hailstones? (paragraph 1) *balls of ice*
What does a hailstone start out as? (paragraph 2) *raindrop*
Where is the layer of cold air found in the summer? (paragraph 2) *just above the earth*
When does the raindrop freeze? (paragraph 2) *when it falls through the cold air*
Why can hailstones do great damage? (paragraph 2) *because they are big and heavy*

Reading for Understanding
4. Write yes or no in the blank.
A hailstorm can be described as
yes deadly   *no* beautiful
yes damaging   *yes* terrible
yes scary   *yes* exciting
yes harmful   *yes* dangerous

Fiery Visitors from Outer Space

Main Idea
1. Choose another title for this story.
____ Travel in Space
_X_ Shooting Stars
____ A Meteorite in Africa

Sequencing
2. Number the events below in the order that they happen.
_4_ We see a "shooting star."
_2_ As it passes through the air, it gets very hot.
_3_ It starts to glow and begins to burn.
_1_ A meteor comes close to the earth and starts to fall.

Reading for Details
3. Use the clues to answer these questions.
When might you see a meteor? (paragraph 1) *on a clear summer night*
What are meteors made of? (paragraph 2) *pieces of rock and metal*
Where do some meteors come from? (paragraph 2) *from comets*
When don't meteors glow? (paragraph 2) *when they are in space*
How do meteors glow when they get close to earth? (paragraph 2) *As they pass through the air they get very hot and burn.*

Reading for Understanding
4. Place the correct letter in the space.
c Meteor   a. a famous swarm of meteors
d Swarm   b. a meteor that has reached the earth
a Perseid   c. the real name for a shooting star
b Meteorite   d. a group of meteors

Answer Key

Giants of the Forest

Name _____

Main Idea
1. Choose another title for the story.
   - X The Redwood Forest
   - ___ Fun in the Forest
   - ___ A Slow - Growing Tree

Sequencing
2. Number the events below in the order that you read about them.
   - 4 Fire does not hurt redwood trees.
   - 1 Redwood trees grow near the Pacific Ocean in California and Oregon.
   - 2 Trees get water from the fog.
   - 3 Insects cannot hurt redwoods.

Reading for Details
3. Use the clues to answer these questions.
   - What are the tallest trees in the world? (paragraph 2) _Redwoods_
   - How big is the tallest redwood? (paragraph 2) _taller than a 20 story building_
   - Where do redwood trees grow? (paragraph 2) _California and Oregon_
   - When does the fog come in? (paragraph 3) _every day_
   - Why can't insects hurt the inside of the redwood trees? (paragraph 3) _because they have very thick bark_

Reading for Understanding
4. Check the correct answer(s).
   Fires do not start easily in redwood forests because
   - X their bark must get very hot in order to burn.
   - X their needles and branches, which burn easily, are far up off the ground.
   - X not many plants grow under the redwoods.
   - ___ few people go into redwood forests.

The Florida Key Deer

Name _____

Main Idea
1. Choose another title for this story.
   - X The Deer that Almost Disappeared
   - ___ The National Key Deer Refuge
   - ___ The Florida Keys

Sequencing
2. Number the events below in the order that they happened.
   - 1 Hunters killed the Key deer.
   - 3 The United States government bought land for a refuge.
   - 2 Some people bought land to use as a shelter.
   - 4 The Key deer spread from five islands to eighteen islands.

Reading for Details
3. Use the clues to answer these questions.
   - Who gets angry at the white-tailed deer for eating crops and gardens? (paragraph 1) _farmers_
   - What is the name of the white-tailed deer's cousin? (paragraph 1) _Florida Key Deer_
   - Where are white-tailed deer found? (paragraph 2) _in forests and grassy countryside from Canada to S. America_
   - When did lots of Key deer live in the forest on the Keys? (paragraph 3) _a hundred years ago_
   - Why were less than forty deer left by 1947? (paragraph 3) _The hunters killed them._

Reading for Understanding
4. Choose the topic for paragraph 2.
   - ___ an ordinary white-tailed deer
   - X the Florida Key deer
   - ___ what Florida Key deer eat

Tasting — A Team Effort

Name _____

Main Idea
1. Choose another title for this story.
   - ___ Eating With Gusto
   - X Why We Taste Food
   - ___ The Four Flavors

Sequencing
2. Number the events below in the order that they happen.
   - 1 You breathe the food oils in.
   - 3 The nose hairs send signals to the brain.
   - 2 The oils land on the small hairs inside your nose.
   - 4 You smell the food.

Reading for Details
3. Use the clues to answer these questions.
   - Who can taste only four flavors? (paragraph 1) _people_
   - What are the little bumps on your tongue called? (paragraph 2) _taste buds_
   - Where do you taste sweet things on your tongue? (paragraph 2) _the tip_
   - When do you think of a special smell as taste? (paragraph 3) _when you are eating_
   - Why can't you taste food very well when you have a cold? (paragraph 3) _food oils cannot get into your nose_

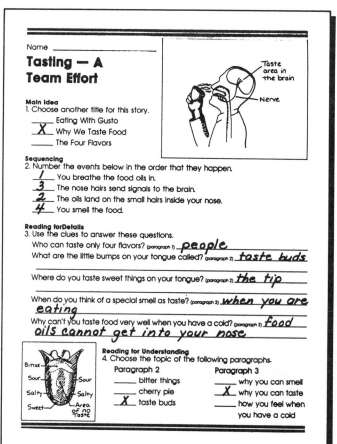

Reading for Understanding
4. Choose the topic of the following paragraphs.

Paragraph 2
- ___ bitter things
- ___ cherry pie
- X taste buds

Paragraph 3
- ___ why you can smell
- X why you can taste
- ___ how you feel when you have a cold

The Baker's Friend

Name _____

Main Idea
1. This story explains
   - X how yeast makes bread rise.
   - ___ why a baker bakes bread.
   - ___ where yeast plants come from.

Sequencing
2. Number the events below in the order that they happen.
   - 2 The yeast plants use the flour and sugar for food.
   - 3 The yeast plants give off alcohol and gas as they grow.
   - 1 Bakers add yeast to bread dough.
   - 4 The bread dough is baked into a fresh, light loaf of bread.

Reading for Details
3. Use the clues to answer these questions.
   - Who adds the yeast to the bread? (paragraph 2) _the baker_
   - What is yeast? (paragraph 2) _millions of tiny plants_
   - What does a yeast plant look like under a microscope? (paragraph 2) _a round gray pillow_
   - When do yeast plants seem to be dead? (paragraph 3) _when they are kept dry_
   - Why are many bakers proud? (paragraph 5) _because of their light, tasty bread_

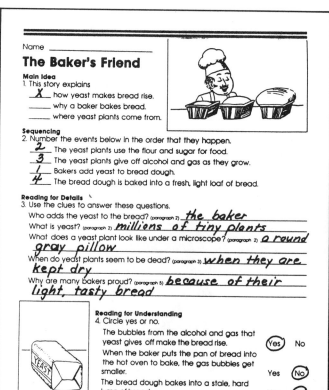

Reading for Understanding
4. Circle yes or no.
   - The bubbles from the alcohol and gas that yeast gives off make the bread rise. **(Yes)** No
   - When the baker puts the pan of bread into the hot oven to bake, the gas bubbles get smaller. Yes **(No)**
   - The bread dough bakes into a stale, hard lump of bread. Yes **(No)**
   - Yeast is not green. **(Yes)** No
   - Yeast does not have leaves or flowers. **(Yes)** No

Answer Key

Quiet! A Fish May Be Listening

Main Idea
1. Choose another title for this story.
   _____ The Lateral Line of a Fish
   _____ The Careful Fisherman
   __X__ Fish Hearing

Sequencing
2. Number the events below in the order that they happen.
   _2_ The air bladder sends the sound to a box in the fish's ear.
   _4_ When the otoliths move, the fish hears the sound.
   _3_ The otoliths move when the sound enters the box.
   _1_ The sound enters the air bladder.

Reading for Details
3. Use the clues to answer these questions.
   Who might say "Be quiet!" while you are fishing? (paragraph 1) _a friend_

   What is the name of the special bag inside the fish's body? (paragraph 2) _air bladder_
   Where are the otoliths? (paragraph 2) _inside a box in the fish's ear_
   When do the otoliths move? (paragraph 2) _when sound comes into the box_
   Why is it important not to splash when you are fishing? (paragraph 5) _so the fish will not hear you and swim away_

Reading for Understanding
4. Circle the correct answer.
   My ears have (one, (two)) jobs.
   My ears keep me ((upright), upside down) in the water.
   My ears have (two, (three)) hollow bones shaped like horseshoes in them.
   My other special organ is called the ((lateral line), longitunal line) which helps me to hear too.

Page 59

Your Personal Mark

Main Idea
1. Choose another title for this story.
   __X__ Your Fingerprints
   _____ Your Skin
   _____ Monkeys and Apes

Sequencing
2. Number the events below in the order that you read about them.
   _4_ Fingerprints help police catch criminals.
   _2_ No two people have the same pattern of fingerprints.
   _1_ Wrinkles on people's fingers form patterns of loops and spirals.
   _3_ Fingerprints stay the same all of a person's life.

Reading for Details
3. Use the clues to answer these questions.
   Who uses fingerprints to catch criminals and find missing people? (paragraph 5) _the police_
   What causes fingerprints? (paragraph 2) _The top skin is so tight that it makes the bottom layer wrinkle._
   Where are your fingerprints located? (paragraph 2) _on the tips of your fingers_
   When do your fingerprints change? (paragraph 4) _never_
   Why are fingerprints different for each person? (paragraph 4) _The pattern of loops and spirals is different for each person._

Reading for Understanding
4. You have learned many things about fingerprints. Check the things that are correct.
   __X__ Fingerprints are special.
   _____ Twins have the same fingerprints.
   __X__ The top layer of skin on the fingertips is so tight that it makes the bottom layer wrinkle.
   _____ Monkeys and apes have their own fingerprints.
   __X__ The wrinkles are the fingerprints.

Page 61

Mysterious Sunspots

Main Idea
1. This story tells about
   _____ the Aurora Borealis.
   _____ ozones.
   __X__ sunspots.

Sequencing
2. Number the events below in the order that they happened.
   _1_ Galileo invented the telescope.
   _3_ Astronomers studied the sunspots.
   _4_ They decided that sunspots were huge storms on the sun.
   _2_ Galileo saw large black spots on the sun.

Reading for Details
3. Use the clues to answer these questions.
   What are sunspots? (paragraph 2) _huge storms on the sun_

   Where are sunspots located? (paragraph 2) _on the sun_

   Why do sunspots look black to us? (paragraph 2) _As gases shoot out from the sun, they cool off and do not glow._
   What changes are caused by sunspots? (paragraph 3) _northern lights, weather, radio signals_
   Who studies sunspots? (paragraph 2) _astronomers_

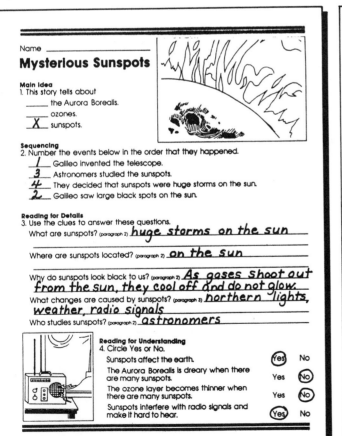

Reading for Understanding
4. Circle Yes or No.

Sunspots affect the earth.	(Yes)	No
The Aurora Borealis is dreary when there are many sunspots.	Yes	(No)
The ozone layer becomes thinner when there are many sunspots.	Yes	(No)
Sunspots interfere with radio signals and make it hard to hear.	(Yes)	No

Page 63

The Sun Followers

Main Idea
1. This story explains
   __X__ how plants move.
   _____ how the sun comes up in the east.
   _____ how plants make food with sunshine.

Sequencing
2. Number the events below in the order that they happen.
   _2_ The cells in the shaded west side of the stem begin to make auxins.
   _4_ The plant bends to face the sun.
   _1_ In the morning, the east side of the plant stem is in the light.
   _3_ The west side of the stem grows fast.

Reading for Details
3. Use the clues to answer these questions.
   Why do plants move? (paragraph 1 & 3) _to move toward the sunlight_
   What chemical helps plants move? (paragraph 2) _auxins_
   Where are auxins located? (paragraph 2) _in the plant cells_
   When are auxins produced by the plant? (paragraph 2) _when a side of a plant is in the shade_
   How do leaves use sunlight? (paragraph 3) _to make food for the plant_

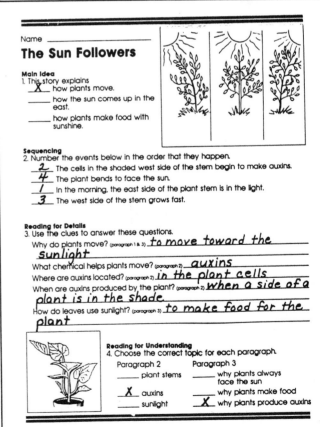

Reading for Understanding
4. Choose the correct topic for each paragraph.
   Paragraph 2
   _____ plant stems
   __X__ auxins
   _____ sunlight

   Paragraph 3
   _____ why plants always face the sun
   _____ why plants make food
   __X__ why plants produce auxins

Page 65

Answer Key

The Earth's Safety Blanket

Main Idea
1. This story explains
   - ___ the use of spray cans.
   - _X_ the ozone layer of the atmosphere.
   - ___ the dangerous rays of the sun.

Sequencing
2. Number the events below in the order that they happened.
   - _3_ Spray cans were changed to contain safe gases.
   - _2_ Scientists became worried about the ozone layer.
   - _1_ People using spray cans were destroying the ozone layer.
   - _4_ The ozone layer was no longer being harmed by spray cans.

Reading for Details
3. Use the clues to answer these questions.
   What is the atmosphere made of? (paragraph 2) *many gases, especially nitrogen and oxygen*
   Where is the atmosphere thick and heavy? (paragraph 2) *close to the earth*
   Where is it thinner? (paragraph 2) *farther from the earth*
   Why is the ozone layer important to the earth? (paragraph 3) *It soaks up dangerous rays from the sun.*
   How was the ozone layer being harmed? (paragraph 1) *from gases in spray cans*

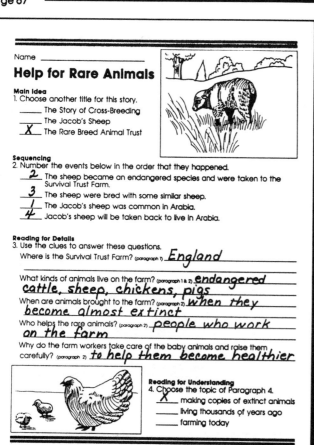

Reading for Understanding
4. Place the correct letter in the blank.
   - _c_ ozone layer — a. thick blanket of air that covers the earth
   - _a_ atmosphere — b. groups of three oxygen atoms
   - _b_ ozone — c. place high in the atmosphere where regular oxygen changes to ozone
   - _d_ spray cans — d. used to contain harmful gases

Page 67

The Ups and Downs of the Barometer

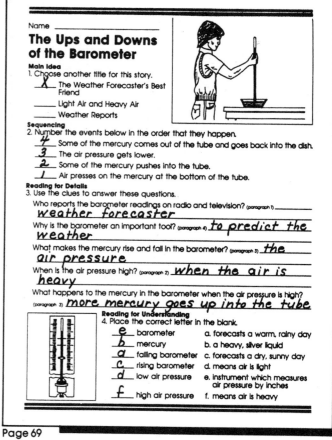

Main Idea
1. Choose another title for this story.
   - _X_ The Weather Forecaster's Best Friend
   - ___ Light Air and Heavy Air
   - ___ Weather Reports

Sequencing
2. Number the events below in the order that they happen.
   - _4_ Some of the mercury comes out of the tube and goes back into the dish.
   - _3_ The air pressure gets lower.
   - _2_ Some of the mercury pushes into the tube.
   - _1_ Air presses on the mercury at the bottom of the tube.

Reading for Details
3. Use the clues to answer these questions.
   Who reports the barometer readings on radio and television? (paragraph 1) *weather forecaster*
   Why is the barometer an important tool? (paragraph 4) *to predict the weather*
   What makes the mercury rise and fall in the barometer? (paragraph 3) *the air pressure*
   When is the air pressure high? (paragraph 2) *when the air is heavy*
   What happens to the mercury in the barometer when the air pressure is high? (paragraph 3) *more mercury goes up into the tube*

Reading for Understanding
4. Place the correct letter in the blank.
   - _e_ barometer — a. forecasts a warm, rainy day
   - _b_ mercury — b. a heavy, silver liquid
   - _a_ falling barometer — c. forecasts a dry, sunny day
   - _c_ rising barometer — d. means air is light
   - _d_ low air pressure — e. instrument which measures air pressure by inches
   - _f_ high air pressure — f. means air is heavy

Page 69

Help for Rare Animals

Main Idea
1. Choose another title for this story.
   - ___ The Story of Cross-Breeding
   - ___ The Jacob's Sheep
   - _X_ The Rare Breed Animal Trust

Sequencing
2. Number the events below in the order that they happened.
   - _2_ The sheep became an endangered species and were taken to the Survival Trust Farm.
   - _3_ The sheep were bred with some similar sheep.
   - _1_ The Jacob's sheep was common in Arabia.
   - _4_ Jacob's sheep will be taken back to live in Arabia.

Reading for Details
3. Use the clues to answer these questions.
   Where is the Survival Trust Farm? (paragraph 1) *England*
   What kinds of animals live on the farm? (paragraph 1 & 2) *endangered cattle, sheep, chickens, pigs*
   When are animals brought to the farm? (paragraph 2) *when they become almost extinct*
   Who helps the rare animals? (paragraph 2) *people who work on the farm*
   Why do the farm workers take care of the baby animals and raise them carefully? (paragraph 2) *to help them become healthier*

Reading for Understanding
4. Choose the topic of Paragraph 4.
   - _X_ making copies of extinct animals
   - ___ living thousands of years ago
   - ___ farming today

Page 71

North America in the Ice Age

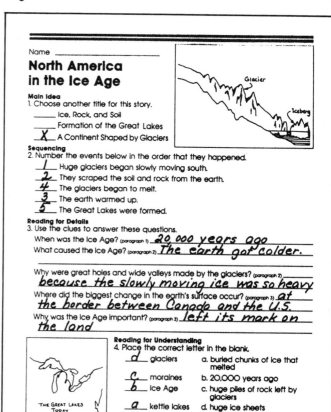

Main Idea
1. Choose another title for this story.
   - ___ Ice, Rock, and Soil
   - ___ Formation of the Great Lakes
   - _X_ A Continent Shaped by Glaciers

Sequencing
2. Number the events below in the order that they happened.
   - _1_ Huge glaciers began slowly moving south.
   - _2_ They scraped the soil and rock from the earth.
   - _4_ The glaciers began to melt.
   - _3_ The earth warmed up.
   - _5_ The Great Lakes were formed.

Reading for Details
3. Use the clues to answer these questions.
   When was the Ice Age? (paragraph 1) *20,000 years ago*
   What caused the Ice Age? (paragraph 2) *The earth got colder.*
   Why were great holes and wide valleys made by the glaciers? (paragraph 2) *because the slowly moving ice was so heavy*
   Where did the biggest change in the earth's surface occur? (paragraph 3) *at the border between Canada and the U.S.*
   Why was the Ice Age important? (paragraph 3) *left its mark on the land*

Reading for Understanding
4. Place the correct letter in the blank.
   - _d_ glaciers — a. buried chunks of ice that melted
   - _c_ moraines — b. 20,000 years ago
   - _b_ Ice Age — c. huge piles of rock left by glaciers
   - _a_ kettle lakes — d. huge ice sheets
   - _e_ Great Lakes — e. huge lakes shaped and filled by melting glaciers

Page 73

Cleaning Up—
How Soap Works

Main Idea
1. Choose another title for this story.
___ Dirt and Grease
___ Washing Your Hands
_X_ The Magic of Soap

Sequencing
2. Number the events below in the order that they happen.
_1_ Soap meets water.
_4_ The dirt becomes surrounded by soap and water.
_5_ The dirt floats away in the water.
_2_ The head end of the soap particle attaches itself to a water molecule.
_3_ The tail end of the soap buries itself into a dirt or grease particle.

Reading for Details.
3. Use the clues to answer these questions.
What works together to wash away dirt? (paragraph 2) _soap and water_

Why does water need help to wash away dirt? (paragraph 2) _It doesn't mix well with dirt._
When do detergents take over? (paragraph 4) _when soap doesn't work well_
Where does the dirt go? (paragraph 3) _It floats away with the water._
Why are soap and detergent such important products? (paragraph 4) _For washing hands and other things_

Reading for Understanding
4. Circle Yes or No.
I make water "wetter." **(Yes)** No
I have a special shape that makes dirt stick to water. **(Yes)** No
My head end attaches to a dirt molecule. Yes **(No)**
My tail end buries itself in a water molecule. Yes **(No)**
My partner, detergent, helps when I just can't do the job. **(Yes)** No

Page 75

Parasites—
Life from Life

Main Idea
1. This story explains
___ how mistletoe takes water from oak trees.
_X_ how parasites take their food from others.
___ how dogs and cats get fleas.

FLEA

TRICHINA WORM LODGED IN MUSCLE FIBER

Sequencing
2. Number the events below in the order that they happen.
_1_ An animal swallows tapeworm eggs.
_3_ The worms attach themselves to the host's intestines.
_4_ The worm uses the food that the animal eats.
_2_ The eggs hatch.
_5_ The host becomes weak.

Reading for Details
3. Use the clues to answer these questions.
How does a parasite get its food? (paragraph 2) _by eating its host while it is alive_
Who is harmed by parasites? (paragraph 2) _hosts_
What is a host? (paragraph 2) _plant or animal in which a parasite lives_
What do plant parasites take from their hosts? (paragraph 2) _sugar_

How is mistletoe different from other plant parasites? (paragraph 2) _It makes its own food._

SHEEP TICK

Reading for Understanding
4. Choose the topic for each paragraph.

Paragraph 2
_X_ how parasites get food
___ how tapeworms grow
___ how mistletoe lives

Paragraph 3
___ what you should know about your dog
_X_ what parasites do to hosts
___ how mistletoe lives

Page 77

The Ghost Fish

Main Idea
1. This story tells about
_X_ a fish that scientists thought was extinct.
___ fishermen in Africa.
___ the Atlantic Ocean.

Sequencing
2. Number the events below in the order that they happened.
_3_ The scientists thought they were seeing a ghost.
_1_ Fishermen in Africa caught a fish.
_4_ Scientists determined the fish to be a coelecanth.
_2_ They took the fish to some scientists.
_5_ More coelecanths were seen by other people.

Reading for Details
3. Use the clues to answer these questions.
What was found in the bottom of the fishing net? (paragraph 1) _the strangest fish they had ever seen_
Why did the fishermen think the fish was strange? (paragraph 2) _The fins looked like very short legs._
Where did the coelecanth live? (paragraph 2) _dark, deep waters_
When did scientists think the coelecanth had died away? (paragraph 3) _300 million years ago_
Why did the coelecanth suddenly appear? (paragraph 3) _to look for more food_

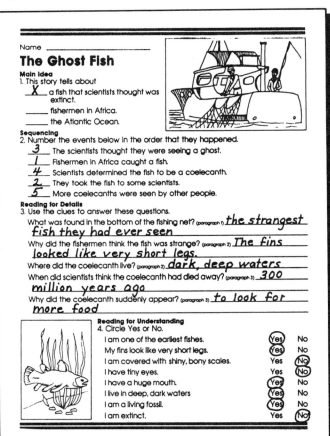

Reading for Understanding
4. Circle Yes or No.
I am one of the earliest fishes. **(Yes)** No
My fins look like very short legs. **(Yes)** No
I am covered with shiny, bony scales. Yes **(No)**
I have tiny eyes. Yes **(No)**
I have a huge mouth. **(Yes)** No
I live in deep, dark waters. **(Yes)** No
I am a living fossil. **(Yes)** No
I am extinct. Yes **(No)**

Page 79

When the Body
Tries Too Hard

Main Idea
1. This story tells about
___ antihistamines.
_X_ allergies.
___ stuffy noses.

Sequencing
2. Number the events below in the order that they happen.
_5_ The person gets watery eyes and a runny nose.
_2_ Antibodies trap the bacteria in the blood.
_1_ Bacteria get into a person's system.
_3_ White blood cells eat the bacteria.
_4_ Special cells make histamine.

Reading for Details
3. Use the clues to answer these questions.
What does the immune system do? (paragraph 1) _It protects the body._
Why do some people get allergies? (paragraph 1) _Their bodies are trying too hard to keep them healthy._
Where are allergy victims likely to go if they get sick enough? (paragraph 3) _to the hospital_
Why does histamine make us uncomfortable? (paragraph 3) _It makes watery eyes and a runny nose._

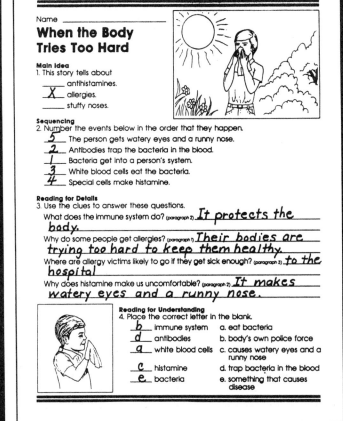

Reading for Understanding
4. Place the correct letter in the blank.
_b_ immune system   a. eat bacteria
_d_ antibodies   b. body's own police force
_a_ white blood cells   c. causes watery eyes and a runny nose
_c_ histamine   d. trap bacteria in the blood
_e_ bacteria   e. something that causes disease

Page 81

Answer Key

A New Old Sport

Main Idea
1. Choose another title for this story.

_____ The Goddess of Skiing

_____ The People of Norway

__X__ Skiing–Transportation and Sport

Sequencing
2. Number the events below in the order that they happened.

__1__ Skiing started in Norway thousands of years ago.

__4__ Skiing became a sport for people in many countries.

__2__ The Laplanders began to follow their reindeer herds on skis.

__3__ Skiing spread from Norway to Sweden and Finland.

Reading for Details
3. Use the clues to answer these questions.

Who are the Laplanders? (paragraph 2) **people in northern Finland**

How do the Laplanders use skis? (paragraph 3) **to follow their reindeer herds**

Where did skiing start? (paragraph 2) **Norway**

When did people begin skiing? (paragraph 2) **thousands of years ago**

What information do we have that tells us when people began skiing? (paragraph 2) **Stone Age carvings and drawings; statues**

Why do people like to ski? (paragraph 6) **for fun**

Reading for Understanding
4. Write the phrase in the correct column.

oldest and most useful, needs a mountain or hill,
walk from place to place, ride ski lifts to the top,
go almost anywhere, exciting trip to the bottom

Cross-country Skiing	Downhill Skiing
oldest and most useful; walk from place to place; go almost anywhere	**needs a mountain; ride ski lifts to the top; exciting trip to the bottom**

Page 83

Buried Treasure

Main Idea
1. This story tells about

__X__ a man who was a treasure hunter.

_____ a big dark spot under the water.

_____ ten Spanish ships that sank in 1715.

Sequencing
2. Number the events below in the order that they happened.

__2__ He read about ten ships that had sunk.

__1__ A man in Florida found a gold coin on the beach.

__3__ He flew an airplane over the ocean.

__4__ He and his friends found one of the ships near the beach.

Reading for Details
3. Use the clues to answer these questions.

Who would not agree that people only find treasure in story books? (paragraph 2) **a man in Florida**

What did he find as he was walking along the beach? (paragraph 2) **an old Spanish gold coin**

Where did he look to find out where the coin came from? (paragraph 3) **old maps, history books**

Why did the man want to know about the gold coin? (paragraph 3) **He was curious and wanted to find out if there were any more.**

When did the ten Spanish ships sink? (paragraph 3) **In 1715 during a storm**

Reading for Understanding
4. Choose the topic for paragraph 2.

Paragraph 2

_____ a Florida beach

__X__ a man who believes in buried treasure

_____ a gold coin

Page 85

A Gift from the Trees

Main Idea
1. This story explains

_____ what kinds of trees have the best sap for syrup.

__X__ how maple syrup is made.

_____ where maple syrup is sold.

Sequencing
2. Number the events below in the order that they happen.

__3__ The syrup makers cook the sap all day.

__4__ The sap gets thick and becomes maple syrup.

__1__ Syrup makers hammer a spout into the tree trunk.

__2__ The sap drops through the spout into a bucket.

Reading for Details
3. Use the clues to answer these questions.

Who made maple syrup a long time ago? (paragraph 1) **Indians in eastern Canada and the northern U.S.**

What kinds of trees have the best sap for syrup? (paragraph 2) **sugar and black maples**

Where do the syrup makers hang the bucket? (paragraph 3) **under the spout**

When do the syrup makers pour the sap into a big pot? (paragraph 3) **when the bucket is full**

Why do the syrup makers boil the sap? (paragraph 3) **to evaporate the water**

Reading for Understanding
4. Check the correct answer(s).

Sugar maples and black maples are used for making maple syrup because

__X__ they are big enough.

_____ they are abundant.

__X__ they have a lot of sap.

__X__ they have the best sap.

Page 87

The Roman Highway

Main Idea
1. Choose another title for this story.

_____ Appius Claudius

_____ American Roads vs. Roman Roads

__X__ Building an Old Highway

Sequencing
2. Number the events below in the order that they happened.

__3__ Appius Claudius checked the work every day.

__4__ Appius Claudius died before the highway was finished.

__2__ Workers started building the highway.

__1__ Emperor Appius Claudius ordered a highway to be built.

Reading for Details
3. Use the clues to answer these questions.

Who built the Appian Way? (paragraph 2) **Appius Claudius**

What materials were used to build the Appian Way? (paragraph 4) **sand, gravel, rock**

When did Appius Claudius order the highway to be built? (paragraph 2) **312 B.C.**

Where is the highway located? (paragraph 2) **between Rome and the southern end of Italy**

Why did Appius Claudius want the highway built? (paragraph 2) **for moving armies and for trade.**

Reading for Understanding
4. Circle the correct answer.

I (could, (could not)) see.

I felt the roadway with my (hands, (feet)) every day to make sure it was smooth.

The highway ((was,) was not) named after me.

In some places, the road is ((1.5 m,) 7.5 m) thick.

Page 89

Answer Key

The First Painters

Main Idea
1. Choose another title for this story.
   _____ Exploring Caves
   _____ How to Make Paints
   __X__ Cave Artists

Sequencing
2. Number the events below in the order that they happened.
   2 They noticed drawings on the wall.
   1 People were exploring caves in Spain.
   4 The scientists determined that the cave people drew them 30,000 years ago.
   3 Scientists then saw the drawings.

Reading for Details
3. Use the clues to answer these questions.
   Who used watercolors to paint pictures 3,000 years ago? (paragraph 1) **Egyptians**
   What did some cave explorers find in 1875? (paragraph 2) **drawings on the walls**
   Where were the caves located in which the pictures were found? (paragraph 2) **Spain**
   When did scientists say the drawings were made? (paragraph 2) **30,000 years ago**
   Why did cave people paint pictures? (paragraph 4) **No one knows for sure.**

Reading for Understanding
4. Check the correct answer(s).

   The cave artists may have painted because
   __X__ they believed that drawing pictures of the animals they hunted would bring them good luck.
   __X__ they thought it was fun.
   __X__ they wanted to decorate their cave walls.

Page 91

A Real Family Tree

Main Idea
1. Choose another title for this story.
   _____ How to Make a Totem Pole
   __X__ History in a Totem Pole
   _____ Indian Ancestors

Sequencing
2. Number the events below in the order that they happen.
   3 Other animals or people important in the clan's stories are carved under the totem.
   2 A picture of the clan's totem is carved on the top of the pole.
   1 Indians form themselves into groups called clans.
   4 The totem pole is set up in the middle of the village where it can be seen from far away.

Reading for Details
3. Use the clues to answer these questions.
   What is a family tree? (paragraph 1) **It tells the names of all your relatives as far back as anyone can remember.**
   What are family trees called that are made from real trees? (paragraph 1) **totem poles**
   Where do the Indian tribes live who make totem poles? (paragraph 1) **western Canada and the western U.S.**
   What is the "totem" of the clan? (paragraph 2) **the animal or plant that started the clan**
   Why are totem poles important? (paragraph 4) **They help a clan remember its history and teach it to its children.**

Reading for Understanding
4. Choose the topic for paragraph 3.
   _____ how the clan shows its history
   _____ where a clan sets up its totem pole
   __X__ how the clan makes its totem pole

Page 93

The Fastest Mail in the West

Main Idea
1. Choose another title for this story.
   __X__ The Pony Express
   _____ The Telegraph
   _____ The U.S. Government in 1860

Sequencing
2. Number the events below in the order that they happened.
   2 Fifteen miles later he would come to a little station.
   1 The rider would gallop off alone from St. Joseph.
   4 The rider would ride for one hundred miles.
   3 There the rider got a fresh horse.
   5 A new rider would take over.

Reading for Details
3. Use the clues to answer these questions.
   Who started the Pony Express? (paragraph 2) **U.S. government**
   Why was the Pony Express started? (paragraph 1) **The stagecoach was too slow.**
   What was the mail carried in? (paragraph 2) **saddlebags**
   Where was the Pony Express route located? (paragraph 2) **between St. Joseph, Missouri and California**
   When was the Pony Express replaced by the telegraph? (paragraph 3) **in 1861 after only one year of service**

Reading for Understanding
4. Place the correct letter in the space.
   b stage coach   a. move mail quickly
   c Pony Express   b. moved mail slowly
   d telegraph   c. moved mail over a 1,000 miles in 10 days
   a trucks and planes   d. replaced the Pony Express

Page 95

The Iroquois— Six as One

Main Idea
1. Choose another title for this story.
   _____ Farmers and Hunters
   _____ The Iroquois Fight Against the Americans
   __X__ The Six Nations of the Iroquois

Sequencing
2. Number the events below in the order that they happened.
   1 Five Indian tribes moved to the area that is now New York.
   5 After the Revolutionary War, the Americans punished the Iroquois for siding with the British.
   3 The Tuscarora tribe joined the Iroquois.
   2 The five tribes united into one great nation called the Iroquois.
   4 The Iroquois fought against the Americans in the Revolutionary War.

Reading for Details
3. Use the clues to answer these questions.
   What were the names of the five tribes that united? (paragraph 2) **Seneca, Oneida, Mohawks, Onendaga, Cayuga**
   When did the sixth tribe join them? (paragraph 2) **1722**
   Why did the tribes unite? (paragraph 2) **They hoped to keep their land.**
   Where did the Iroquois settle? (paragraph 1) **New York**
   How did the Americans punish the Iroquois? (paragraph 3) **by sending them to a different part of North America**

Reading for Understanding
4. Place the correct letter in the blank.
   a blowgun   a. favorite weapon
   d longhouses   b. last tribe to join the Iroquois nation
   b Tuscarora   c. friends of the Iroquois
   c British   d. long, bark-covered houses

Page 97

Answer Key

The History of Names

Main Idea
1. Choose another title for this story.
   - _X_ What's In a Name?
   - _____ The Different Looks of Names
   - _____ Personal History

Sequencing
2. Number the events below in the order that they happened.
   - _4_ People started using last names.
   - _2_ People began to live together in towns.
   - _3_ Sometimes several people would have the same first name.
   - _1_ People only had first names.

Reading for Details
3. Use the clues to answer these questions.
   - Who chooses a child's name? (paragraph 2) _the parents_
   - When did people start using last names? (paragraph 2) _about 900 years ago_
   - How were last names chosen? (paragraph 2) _by using parent's name, by person's job, by where people lived_
   - Where does "John" become "Ivan"? (paragraph 2) _in Russia_
   - Why are names important? (paragraph 4) _to tell something about a person's ancestors and the way they lived_

Reading for Understanding
4. Choose the most likely reason for each of these last names.

Kevin Hill
- _____ He liked to climb hills.
- _____ He was a mountain builder.
- _X_ He lived on a hill.

Ben Johnson
- _____ He lived near a man named John.
- _____ His best friend was named John.
- _X_ He was the son of John.

Caroline Baker
- _____ She liked to bake bread.
- _X_ She was the town baker.
- _____ She lived by a bakery.

Page 99

Covered Bridges

Main Idea
1. Choose another title for this story.
   - _____ Saving an Important Bridge
   - _X_ Tunnels Over Water
   - _____ The World's Longest Covered Bridge

Sequencing
2. Number the events below in the order that they happened.
   - _2_ The whole bridge would have to be replaced.
   - _4_ The idea worked well, and the covered bridges lasted longer.
   - _1_ People found that water and dampness warped the wood of their bridges.
   - _3_ Someone thought of putting a cover over the bridges.
   - _5_ The covered bridge was invented.

Reading for Details
3. Use the clues to answer these questions.
   - Where are most of the covered bridges located today? (paragraph 4) _New Hampshire, Vermount, Ohio_
   - Why are people working to save the covered bridges? (paragraph 4) _so our children and grandchildren can see them_
   - What happened to bridges before covers were added? (paragraph 3) _water and dampness warped the wood._
   - How do covers help the bridges? (paragraph 3) _They protected the wood._
   - Why have many of the covered bridges disappeared? (paragraph 1) _to make room for modern highways_

Reading for Understanding
4. Check the other reasons that covered bridges may have been built.
   - _X_ to keep horses from becoming frightened of the water
   - _____ to make the bridge look pretty
   - _X_ to shelter travelers during bad weather
   - _____ to give children a place to play "haunted house"

Page 101

Carving—an Art

Main Idea
1. This story tells about
   - _____ the use of sculpture in religious ceremonies.
   - _X_ a brief history of the art of sculpture.
   - _____ the Greeks and Romans.

Sequencing
2. Number the events below in the order that they happened.
   - _3_ The Egyptians carved huge sculptures of their pharoahs.
   - _1_ Someone carved a piece of wood with a sharp stone.
   - _4_ Greeks used athletes as models for their sculptures.
   - _2_ People made sculptures to look like the gods they worshipped.
   - _5_ Sculptures were made of stone, metal, or even junk.

Reading for Details
3. Use the clues to answer these questions.
   - Who carved huge statues of their pharoahs? (paragraph 2) _Egyptians_
   - What were the statues made of? (paragraph 2) _stone_
   - Where did the Egyptians believe the spirit of the pharoah would return? (paragraph 2) _to the statue_
   - When did the Egyptians put the statue in the pharoah's tomb? (paragraph 2) _when he died_
   - Why did the Greeks and Romans make sculptures? (paragraph 3) _because they thought sculpture was beautiful art_

Reading for Understanding
4. Put these phrases in the correct column.

do not believe in statues coming to life; used athletes as models; use stone, metal, junk, food, cloth; famous for statues of their gods; used marble; only sculptor knows for sure what it is; soft sculpture

Long Ago	Today
used athletes as models; famous for statues of their gods; used marble	do not believe in statues coming to life; use stone, metal, junk, food, cloth; only sculptor knows...; soft sculpture

Page 103

The Royal Umbrella

Main Idea
1. This story tells about
   - _X_ the history of the umbrella.
   - _____ using an umbrella on a rainy day.
   - _____ a sign of power.

Sequencing
2. Number the events below in the order that they happened.
   - _2_ The Romans used umbrellas as protection from rain.
   - _1_ People in ancient Egypt used umbrellas as sunshades.
   - _5_ People all over Europe used umbrellas.
   - _3_ The umbrella disappeared.
   - _4_ Rich Europeans started using umbrellas.

Reading for Details
3. Use the clues to answer the questions.
   - Who invented the umbrella? (paragraph 1) _Nobody knows._
   - What happened to common people in Egypt who used umbrellas? (paragraph 2) _They were punished._
   - When did the umbrella disappear? (paragraph 3) _when the Roman Empire died away_
   - Where and when did the umbrella reappear? (paragraph 3) _in Italy around 1600_
   - Why are umbrellas used today? (paragraph 4) _as protection from rain_

Reading for Understanding
4. Check the correct statements.
   - _____ At first I was used for protection from shadows.
   - _X_ The Romans were the first ones to use me as protection from the rain.
   - _____ Only poor people could use me.
   - _X_ I was "water-proofed" by covering cloth with oil or plant gum.
   - _X_ Anyone can use me now.

Page 105

Answer Key

The Fighting Spiders of Japan

Main Idea
1. This story tells about
   - **X** the popular game of spider fights in China and Japan.
   - _____ Chinese and Japanese boys at play.
   - _____ male spiders fighting.

Sequencing
2. Number the events below in order.
   - **2** Two boys put their spiders on the table.
   - **4** The winner is named king of the spiders.
   - **1** A group of boys gather in the playground.
   - **3** The spiders see each other and become angry.
   - **5** The owner of the winning spider lets him go free.

Reading for Details
3. Use the clues to answer these questions.
   - Who takes part in the spider contests? (paragraph 1 & 3) *men and boys*
   - How do the boys find their spiders? (paragraph 1) *They search in gardens and bushes.*
   - Where do the boys gather for the contests? (paragraph 2) *playgrounds or houses*
   - When do the spiders become angry? (paragraph 2) *when they see each other*
   - Why does the owner let the winning spider go free? (paragraph 2) *as a reward*

Reading for Understanding
4. Choose the topic for each paragraph.

Paragraph 1	Paragraph 2	Paragraph 3
_____ getting up	_____ king spiders	_____ two men
_____ gardening	**X** spider contests	_____ a town
X looking for fighting spiders	_____ cheers for the winner	**X** a Japanese tradition

Page 107

The Magic Stones

Main Idea
1. This story tells about
   - _____ mysterious powers.
   - **X** birthstones.
   - _____ months of the year.

Sequencing
2. Number the events below in the order that you read about them.
   - **1** Ancient people believed precious stones had mysterious powers.
   - **3** Amethyst was said to cure a headache.
   - **2** Diamonds were said to prevent nightmares.
   - **4** People wearing birthstones are carrying on the idea that certain stones have special powers.

Reading for Details
3. Use the clues to answer the questions.
   - Who believed that precious stones had mysterious powers? (paragraph 1) *people in ancient times*
   - When are people carrying on that idea? (paragraph 1) *when people wear their birthstones*
   - What is an amethyst? (paragraph 2) *a purple stone*
   - What is the birthstone of May? (paragraph 2) *the emerald*
   - Why do people wear their birthstones today? (paragraph 4) *because they think birthstones are beautiful*

Reading for Understanding
4. Place the correct letter in the blank.
   - **d** topaz   a. stands for clear thinking
   - **e** pearl   b. stands for strength
   - **a** sapphire   c. said to be lucky for only those born in October
   - **b** garnet   d. means a good friend
   - **c** opal   e. stands for goodness

Page 109

The Mysteries of Chaco Canyon

Main Idea
1. Choose another title for this story.
   - **X** The Mysterious Calendar
   - _____ The Hiking Trip
   - _____ Life in Chaco Canyon

Sequencing
2. Number the events below in the order that they happened.
   - **4** It was decided that the big spiral was used as a calendar.
   - **2** They discovered the spiral shapes on the wall.
   - **1** Some people were climbing the canyon walls.
   - **3** They noticed that the sunlight made a line on the big spiral.
   - **5** The two small spirals are still being studied.

Reading for Details
3. Use the clues to answer these questions.
   - Who lived in Chaco Canyon 1,000 years ago? (paragraph 1) *Pueblo Indians*
   - What was found on their canyon walls? (paragraph 3) *three spiral shapes*
   - Where did the sunlight shining on the big spiral come from? (paragraph 3) *a crack in the rocks*
   - When does the line of light just touch the outside of the spiral? (paragraph 3) *on the shortest day of the year*
   - When does it touch the exact center of the spiral? (paragraph 3) *on the longest day of the year*
   - Why are the spirals studied today? (paragraph 4) *Small spirals are mysteries.*

Reading for Understanding
4. Circle Yes or No.

I am a member of the Navajo Tribe.	Yes	**No**
I lived in southern Mexico in the Chaco Canyon.	Yes	**No**
I lived by a river.	**Yes**	No
I grew corn and strawberries.	Yes	**No**
I was a peaceful person.	**Yes**	No
I made a calendar on the canyon walls.	**Yes**	No

Page 111

The Story of Spinning

Main Idea
1. This story explains
   - _____ the art of sheering sheep.
   - **X** the art of spinning.
   - _____ the art of making clothes.

Sequencing
2. Number the events below in the order that they happen.
   - **3** The spinning wheel pulls the wool into yarn.
   - **1** The wool is taken from the sheep.
   - **2** The wool must be cleaned and then carded.
   - **4** The yarn is ready for weaving.
   - **5** The cloth is used to make clothing for the family.

Reading for Details
3. Use the clues to answer these questions.
   - Who usually carded the wool? (paragraph 2) *the children*
   - Why did they usually get that job? (paragraph 2) *It is easy.*
   - What tool was used for carding? (paragraph 2) *two wide combs*
   - When was the wool ready for weaving? (paragraph 3) *when it is yarn*
   - Why do some people still spin their own yarn? (paragraph 4) *because they love the old art*

Reading for Understanding
4. Place the correct letter in the blank.
   - **d** carding   a. makes wool fibers straight and smooth
   - **a** combing   b. twisting and stretching the fibers into yarn
   - **b** spinning   c. long winding stick
   - **c** spindle   d. easy but tiresome

Page 113

Myths, Legends, Neat Things IF8713

127

© 1990 Instructional Fair, Inc.